University of Cambridge

Department of Applied Economics

OCCASIONAL PAPERS 13

FORTRAN PROGRAMS FOR ECONOMISTS

D1464646

University of Cambridge

Department of Applied Economics

Occasional Papers

Fortran Programs
for Economists

by LUCY JOAN SLATER
Department of Applied Economics

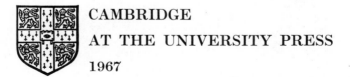

CAMBRIDGE
AT THE UNIVERSITY PRESS
1967

PUBLISHED BY

THE SYNDICS OF THE CAMBRIDGE UNIVERSITY PRESS

Bentley House, 200 Euston Road, London N.W.1

American Branch: 32 East 57th Street, New York, N.Y. 10022

© DEPARTMENT OF APPLIED ECONOMICS
UNIVERSITY OF CAMBRIDGE
1967

$\omega + \alpha$ Set by E.W.C. Wilkins & Associates Ltd., London

Contents

Preface

The aim of this work is to provide for students some simple computer programs in Fortran, which will carry out elementary arithmetic operations on matrices and vectors. In particular, the pamphlet gives a detailed discussion of the processes of matrix inversion, regression analysis, linear programming and survey analysis. In Chapter one, the first section states the facts about matrix algebra in simple arithmetic and mathematical terms. The second section gives the actual computer source program, with its detailed specification and flow diagrams. This section gives actual examples of the input and output of the program. Chapter two follows a similar pattern and deals in a similar way with the techniques of doing regression analysis on an electronic computer. Chapter three deals with linear programming by the simplex process and Chapter four discusses the techniques of doing survey analysis.

One paragraph outlines the language used, Fortran IV, which is a programming language used on most modern computers. Only a very elementary knowledge of programming, computing and algebra is assumed. A student with no previous experience of computer programming is advised to read *A Guide to Fortran Programming* by Danial D. McCracken (published by John Wiley, New York, 1961).

The actual programs described here, were developed and tested by the use of the Fortran IV compiler on the I.C.T. 1906 computer, in the computing laboratory of the University of Essex, by permission of the acting director Professor Ian Proudman. The techniques used in these programs were perfected over a period of twelve years, in the Department of Applied Economics at Cambridge, and tested on the various computers in the Cambridge University Mathematical Laboratory, by kind permission of the director Professor M.V.Wilkes.

L.J.S.

Dec. 1966.
University of Cambridge,
Department of Applied Economics,
Sidgwick Avenue,
Cambridge

1 MATRICES AND VECTORS

ELEMENTARY PROPERTIES OF MATRICES

§1.1 Definitions

Any rectangular array of numbers is called a matrix. For example the array

$$\begin{bmatrix} 1 & 3 & 2 \\ 5 & 7 & 4 \end{bmatrix}$$

which has two rows and three columns is a matrix of type 2×3.

A matrix which has only one row for example

$$[\, 0{\cdot}1 \quad 3{\cdot}2 \quad -0{\cdot}5 \quad 6{\cdot}3 \,]$$

is called a row vector, or simply a vector, and a matrix which has only one column, for example

$$\begin{bmatrix} 5{\cdot}1 \\ 0{\cdot}7 \\ -22{\cdot}5 \end{bmatrix}.$$

is called a column vector. A column vector is sometimes written

$$\{\, 5{\cdot}1 \quad 0{\cdot}7 \quad -22{\cdot}5 \,\}$$

with curved instead of long square brackets. This is done only to save space on the printed page.

Each number in a matrix or vector is called an element of the matrix. A vector with only one element is called a scalar. It is in fact just an ordinary number. The elements of a matrix can be real or complex numbers, other matrices or mathematical functions. The present work is concerned only with matrices which have real numbers for their elements.

If there are m numbers in each column of the matrix and n numbers in each row, we say that the matrix is a matrix of order $m \times n$, that is a matrix of m rows and n columns. The number of rows is always stated before the number of columns.

A vector is usually referred to by a single small letter, for example $a = [0{\cdot}5 \quad 3{\cdot}6 \quad 9{\cdot}8]$, $b = \{-0{\cdot}1 \quad 2{\cdot}3\}$. Each element of a vector has one suffix to show its position in the vector. Thus in the vector a, $a_1 = 0{\cdot}5$, $a_2 = 3{\cdot}6$ and $a_3 = 9{\cdot}8$. In general $a = [a_i]$. A scalar quantity is distinguished from a matrix or a vector by being written as a single small Greek letter, e.g. $\lambda = 3{\cdot}2$.

Each matrix is usually indicated by a single capital letter, and each element is referred to by a small letter followed by two suffixes. This notation is called a double suffix notation. Thus, if a_{ij} is the jth element in the ith row of an $m \times n$ matrix, we can write

$$A = [a_{ij}], \tag{1.1.1}$$

where $i = 1, 2, 3, \ldots, m$ and $j = 1, 2, 3, \ldots, n$. Thus, in the first example above, the first element of the first row is 1. When we call this element a_{11}, we can write $a_{11} = 1$. Similarly, the second element of the first row is $a_{12} = 3$, and the first element of the second row is $a_{21} = 5$.

If $m = n$, that is if the matrix has the same number of elements in its rows as in its columns, it is called a square matrix. If $m \neq n$, the matrix is said to be rectangular. A square matrix of type $n \times n$ is said to be of order n.

A matrix which has been obtained by interchanging the rows and columns of the original matrix, is called the transpose of the original matrix. It is indicated by the same capital letter but with a dash added, thus if

$$A = \begin{bmatrix} 1 & 3 & 2 \\ 5 & 7 & 4 \end{bmatrix}$$

then
$$A' = \begin{bmatrix} 1 & 5 \\ 3 & 7 \\ 2 & 4 \end{bmatrix} \text{ is its transpose.} \tag{1.1.2}$$

If the original matrix is of order $m \times n$, that is with m rows of n items in each row, then the transposed matrix is of order $n \times m$, that is with n rows of m items in each row. In the subscript notation, if $A = [a_{ij}]$, then $A' = [a_{ji}] = [a_{ij}]'$.

In print, matrices and vectors are usually distinguished by the use of the heavy Clarendon type. Alternatively, in hand written or typed work a bar is often written above a letter to indicate a vector or a matrix, thus $\bar{a} = [a_i]$.

A diagonal matrix is a square matrix, in which all the elements are zero except those elements which fall on the main diagonal. For example,

$$\hat{a} = \begin{bmatrix} 1 & 0 & 0 \\ 0 & 5 & 0 \\ 0 & 0 & 3 \end{bmatrix} \text{ is a diagonal matrix.} \tag{1.1.3}$$

This type of matrix is often represented in print by a circumflex over a letter, as above.

The commonest diagonal matrix is the unit matrix. This has units down the main diagonal and zero elements everywhere else. It is usually represented by a capital I. Thus

$$I = \begin{bmatrix} 1 & 0 & 0 \\ 0 & 1 & 0 \\ 0 & 0 & 1 \end{bmatrix}. \tag{1.1.4}$$

This is a unit matrix of order 3.

A diagonal matrix is unaltered by interchange of its rows and columns, so that a diagonal matrix is equal to its own transpose, and we have

$$\hat{a}' = \hat{a} \quad \text{and} \quad I' = I. \tag{1.1.5}$$

A matrix which has the elements in corresponding positions about the

10

diagonal equal to one another, is called a symmetric matrix. Thus

$$A = \begin{bmatrix} 1 & 2 & 6 \\ 2 & 3 & 7 \\ 6 & 7 & 5 \end{bmatrix} \text{ is a symmetric matrix.} \tag{1.1.6}$$

The general definition of a symmetric matrix is $A = [a_{ij}]$ where $a_{ij} = a_{ji}$ for all values of i and j. Addition or subtraction of matrices or vectors of the same type can be carried out in the same way as with ordinary numbers, simply by adding or subtracting the corresponding elements in each row or column. Thus

$$[1 \quad 5 \quad 7] + [2 \quad 3 \quad 4] = [3 \quad 8 \quad 11] \tag{1.1.7}$$

and

$$\begin{bmatrix} 1 & 3 & 2 \\ 5 & 1 & 7 \end{bmatrix} + \begin{bmatrix} 0 & 9 & -3 \\ 2 & -3 & 7 \end{bmatrix} = \begin{bmatrix} 1 & 12 & -1 \\ 7 & -2 & 14 \end{bmatrix}. \tag{1.1.8}$$

Matrices and vectors can also be multiplied or divided by ordinary numbers, that is by scalars. For example,

$$4 \times [0 \cdot 1 \quad 0 \cdot 2 \quad 0 \cdot 3] = [0 \cdot 4 \quad 0 \cdot 8 \quad 1 \cdot 2] \tag{1.1.9}$$

and

$$\begin{bmatrix} 1 & 3 & 2 \\ 5 & 1 & 7 \end{bmatrix} = \frac{1}{2} \times \begin{bmatrix} 2 & 6 & 4 \\ 10 & 2 & 14 \end{bmatrix}. \tag{1.1.10}$$

§1.2 Multiplication of vectors and matrices

A row vector and a column vector can be multiplied together provided that they both have the same number of elements. The result is a scalar, an ordinary number. The rule for multiplication of two vectors is:

the inner product of a row vector and a column vector is
the sum of all the products of their elements.

For example

$$[1 \quad 3 \quad 5] \times \{2 \quad 4 \quad 6\} = 1 \times 2 + 3 \times 4 + 5 \times 6,$$
$$= 44.$$

In mathematical notation; if $a = [a_i]$ and $b = [b_i]$ are two vectors each with n elements, then their inner product is the scalar

$$c = a \times b' = a_1 b_1 + a_2 b_2 + \dots \dots + a_n b_n. \tag{1.2.1}$$

If we introduce the symbol for summation, from $i = 1$ to $i = n$, this is

$$c = a \times b' = \sum_{i=1}^{n} a_i b_i. \tag{1.2.2}$$

Matrix multiplication is a rather more complicated process, than vector multiplication, as we have two dimensions to consider instead of only one. It can be carried out only if the number of columns in matrix A is equal to the number of rows in matrix B. Let us consider an example.

11

If
$$A = \begin{bmatrix} 1 & 3 & 7 \\ 2 & 5 & 0 \end{bmatrix}$$
with two rows and three columns,

and
$$B = \begin{bmatrix} 3 & 2 \\ 11 & 9 \\ 1 & 6 \end{bmatrix}$$
with three rows and two columns,

then

$$A \times B = \begin{bmatrix} 1 \times 3 + 3 \times 11 + 7 \times 1 & 1 \times 2 + 3 \times 9 + 7 \times 6 \\ 2 \times 3 + 5 \times 11 + 0 \times 1 & 2 \times 2 + 5 \times 9 + 0 \times 6 \end{bmatrix}$$

$$= \begin{bmatrix} 43 & 71 \\ 61 & 49 \end{bmatrix}, \text{ with two rows and two columns.}$$

Here each element of the new matrix is the product of a row vector from A and a column vector from B.

Now let us try to multiply together the same two matrices, but in the reverse order. We find that

$$B \times A = \begin{bmatrix} 3 \times 1 + 2 \times 2 & 3 \times 3 + 2 \times 5 & 3 \times 7 + 2 \times 0 \\ 11 \times 1 + 9 \times 2 & 11 \times 3 + 9 \times 5 & 11 \times 7 + 9 \times 0 \\ 1 \times 1 + 1 \times 2 & 1 \times 3 + 1 \times 5 & 1 \times 7 + 1 \times 0 \end{bmatrix}$$

$$= \begin{bmatrix} 7 & 19 & 21 \\ 29 & 78 & 77 \\ 3 & 8 & 7 \end{bmatrix}.$$

This is an entirely different result from the first one, and the new matrix has now three rows and three columns. So the product $A \times B$ is not the same as the product $B \times A$. Here each element of the new matrix is the product of a row vector from B and a column vector from A. Unlike ordinary numbers, the order in which the multiplication is carried out affects the result.

In the first case, $A \times B$, the matrix A is said to be post-multiplied by the matrix B, and B is pre-multiplied by A. In the second case, $B \times A$, the matrix B is said to be post-multiplied by A and A is pre-multiplied by B.

The rule for forming the jth element in the ith row of the matrix $C = A \times B$ is:

form the sum of the products of each element of the ith row of A, multiplied by the corresponding element of the jth column of B.

In mathematical terms, let

$$[c_{ij}] = [a_{ij}] \times [b_{ij}] \qquad (1.2.3)$$

where $[a_{ij}]$ has m rows and n columns, and $[b_{ij}]$ has n rows and p columns. Then

$$c_{ij} = \sum_{k=1}^{n} a_{ik} b_{kj} \qquad (1.2.4)$$

and $[c_{ij}]$ has m rows and p columns.

We cannot form $D = B \times A$ unless $p = m$, that is unless the number of columns

12

in B equals the number of rows in A. In that case

$$[d_{ij}] = [b_{ij}] \times [a_{ij}] \qquad (1.2.5)$$

where

$$d_{ij} = \sum_{k=1}^{m} b_{ik} a_{kj} \qquad (1.2.6)$$

and $[d_{ij}]$ has n rows and n columns.

Any number of matrices can be multiplied together, provided that they have matching numbers of rows and columns. Thus: if

$$A = \begin{bmatrix} 1 & 3 & 7 \\ 2 & 5 & 0 \end{bmatrix}, \quad B = \begin{bmatrix} 3 & 2 & 4 \\ 11 & 9 & 5 \\ 1 & 6 & 7 \end{bmatrix} \quad \text{and} \quad C = \begin{bmatrix} 1 & 2 \\ 3 & 5 \\ 7 & 0 \end{bmatrix},$$

then $A \times B \times C = (A \times B) \times C$

$$= \begin{bmatrix} 1\times3 + 3\times11 + 7\times1 & 1\times2 + 3\times9 + 7\times6 & 1\times4 + 3\times5 + 7\times7 \\ 2\times3 + 5\times11 + 0\times7 & 2\times2 + 5\times9 + 0\times6 & 2\times4 + 5\times5 + 0\times7 \end{bmatrix} \times \begin{bmatrix} 1 & 2 \\ 3 & 5 \\ 7 & 0 \end{bmatrix}$$

$$= \begin{bmatrix} 43 & 71 & 68 \\ 61 & 49 & 33 \end{bmatrix} \times \begin{bmatrix} 1 & 2 \\ 3 & 5 \\ 7 & 0 \end{bmatrix}$$

$$= \begin{bmatrix} 43\times1 + 71\times3 + 68\times7 & 43\times2 + 71\times5 + 68\times0 \\ 61\times1 + 49\times3 + 33\times7 & 61\times2 + 49\times5 + 33\times0 \end{bmatrix}$$

$$= \begin{bmatrix} 732 & 441 \\ 439 & 367 \end{bmatrix}.$$

The reader can check for himself that $A \times (B \times C)$, that is pre-multiplying C by B and then pre-multiplying the result by A, gives exactly the same result as $(A \times B) \times C$ above, but that $(B \times A) \times C$ does not give the same result, as now B is post-multiplied by A instead of pre-multiplied by A.

We can see now why above, we used the term 'inner product' of a row and column vector, rather than just 'product'. As with the multiplication of matrices, the order in which a row and a column vector are multiplied together affects the result. The outer product of a column vector multiplied by a row vector with the same number of elements n is a matrix of order $n \times n$. Thus

$$\{1 \quad 3 \quad 5\} \times [2 \quad 4 \quad 6] = \begin{bmatrix} 2 & 4 & 6 \\ 6 & 12 & 18 \\ 10 & 20 & 30 \end{bmatrix}$$

and in general the outer product of two vectors of order n is

$$\{a_i\}[b_j] = [a_i b_j] \qquad (1.2.7)$$

whereas the inner product is

$$[a_i]\{b_j\} = \sum_{k=1}^{n} a_k b_k. \qquad (1.2.8)$$

13

§1.3 Matrix inversion

The inversion of matrices corresponds to the division of ordinary numbers, but it is a very much more complicated process. We can find the inverse of a square matrix only, not of a rectangular one. The symbol A^{-1} is used to indicate the inverse of a square matrix A of order $n \times n$. The problem of inversion is then the problem of finding a square matrix A^{-1} also of order $n \times n$, such that $A \times A^{-1} = I$, the unit matrix of order $n \times n$.

The process of inverting a square matrix of any size is closely connected with the problem of solving a set of linear equations, so we shall consider the calculation from this viewpoint first. Let us take the pair of equations

$$y + 2z = w$$
$$5y + 7z = x \tag{1.3.1}$$

where y and z are the unknown quantities, but w and x are known quantities. If we bring the largest coefficient to the leading position by interchanging the order of the equations and rewriting their elements in a different order, this leads to

$$7z + 5y = x$$
$$2z + y = w. \tag{1.3.2}$$

Next let us divide the first equation throughout by its first coefficient, and the second equation throughout by its first coefficient. Then we have

$$z + \frac{5}{7}y = \frac{1}{7}x$$
$$z + \frac{1}{2}y = \frac{1}{2}w. \tag{1.3.3}$$

Hence, by the subtraction of the second equation from the first one, we have eliminated z and we have

$$\frac{10 - 7}{14}y = \frac{1}{7}x - \frac{1}{2}w \tag{1.3.4}$$

as our second equation. So, on dividing throughout by the coefficient of y, we find that

$$y = \frac{2}{3}x - \frac{7}{3}w. \tag{1.3.5}$$

This result expresses the unknown quantity y in terms of the known quantities x and w. If now we substitute this value of y back into the equation for z, we have

$$z + \frac{5}{7}\left(\frac{2}{3}x - \frac{7}{3}w\right) = \frac{1}{7}x,$$

that is

$$z = -\frac{1}{3}x + \frac{5}{3}w. \tag{1.3.6}$$

This result expresses the unknown quantity z in terms of the known quantities x and w. On interchanging the order of our rows and columns back to their original order, we find as our answers

14

$$y = -\frac{7}{3}w + \frac{2}{3}x$$

and
$$z = \frac{5}{3}w + \frac{1}{3}x. \qquad (1.3.7)$$

Let us rewrite this process in full, in matrix form. The original equations are

$$\begin{bmatrix} 1 & 2 \\ 5 & 7 \end{bmatrix} \times \begin{bmatrix} y \\ z \end{bmatrix} = \begin{bmatrix} 1 & 0 \\ 0 & 1 \end{bmatrix} \times \begin{bmatrix} w \\ x \end{bmatrix}. \qquad (1.3.8)$$

They become

$$\begin{bmatrix} 7 & 5 \\ 2 & 1 \end{bmatrix} \times \begin{bmatrix} z \\ y \end{bmatrix} = \begin{bmatrix} 1 & 0 \\ 0 & 1 \end{bmatrix} \times \begin{bmatrix} x \\ w \end{bmatrix} \qquad (1.3.9)$$

when we bring the largest element to the leading position by the interchange of rows and columns.

Next let us divide each element of the first row by the element in its first column, to obtain a 1 (one) in the first place in the first column, and next let us subtract each element of the first row multiplied by the first element of the second row from the corresponding element in the second row, so as to obtain a 0 (nought) in the first position of the second row,

$$\begin{bmatrix} 1 & \frac{5}{7} \\ 0 & -\frac{3}{14} \end{bmatrix} \times \begin{bmatrix} z \\ y \end{bmatrix} = \begin{bmatrix} \frac{1}{7} & 0 \\ -\frac{1}{7} & \frac{1}{2} \end{bmatrix} \times \begin{bmatrix} x \\ w \end{bmatrix}. \qquad (1.3.10)$$

Now divide across the second row, by the coefficient on its diagonal, $\frac{-3}{14}$, to obtain a 1 (one) on this diagonal.

$$\begin{bmatrix} 1 & \frac{5}{7} \\ 0 & 1 \end{bmatrix} \times \begin{bmatrix} z \\ y \end{bmatrix} = \begin{bmatrix} \frac{1}{7} & 0 \\ \frac{2}{3} & -\frac{7}{3} \end{bmatrix} \times \begin{bmatrix} x \\ w \end{bmatrix}. \qquad (1.3.11)$$

Our original matrix has now been reduced to what is called triangular form, that is with 1's down the diagonal and 0's beneath the diagonal. We next perform the operation known as back-substitution. That is, we subtract the elements of the second row multiplied by the coefficient 5/7 in the last position of the first row, from the corresponding elements of the first row, so that we have a 0 (nought) in the last position on the first row,

$$\begin{bmatrix} 1 & 0 \\ 0 & 1 \end{bmatrix} \times \begin{bmatrix} z \\ y \end{bmatrix} = \begin{bmatrix} -\frac{1}{3} & \frac{5}{3} \\ \frac{2}{3} & -\frac{7}{3} \end{bmatrix} \times \begin{bmatrix} x \\ w \end{bmatrix}. \qquad (1.3.12)$$

Finally we interchange our rows and columns back to their original order and find our result in the form

$$\begin{bmatrix} 1 & 0 \\ 0 & 1 \end{bmatrix} \times \begin{bmatrix} y \\ z \end{bmatrix} = \begin{bmatrix} -\frac{7}{3} & \frac{2}{3} \\ \frac{5}{3} & -\frac{1}{3} \end{bmatrix} \times \begin{bmatrix} w \\ x \end{bmatrix}, \qquad (1.3.13)$$

that is, we have calculated the inverse matrix

$$\begin{bmatrix} 1 & 2 \\ 5 & 7 \end{bmatrix}^{-1} = \begin{bmatrix} -\dfrac{7}{3} & \dfrac{2}{3} \\ \dfrac{5}{3} & -\dfrac{1}{3} \end{bmatrix}. \tag{1.3.14}$$

We must now check by multiplication of these two matrices that in fact

$$\begin{bmatrix} 1 & 2 \\ 5 & 7 \end{bmatrix} \times \begin{bmatrix} -\dfrac{7}{3} & \dfrac{2}{3} \\ \dfrac{5}{3} & -\dfrac{1}{3} \end{bmatrix} = \begin{bmatrix} 1\times(-7/3) + 2\times(5/3) & 1\times(2/3) + 2\times(-1/3) \\ 5\times(-7/3) + 7\times(5/3) & 5\times(2/3) + 7\times(-1/3) \end{bmatrix}$$

$$= \begin{bmatrix} 1 & 0 \\ 0 & 1 \end{bmatrix}. \tag{1.3.15}$$

This process provides us with a means in theory, of inverting any size of matrix, but in practice, the calculation quickly becomes very laborious using hand-calculating machines. We will go through the rules again, illustrating them by the inversion of a 3×3 matrix.

(i) Write down the matrix to be inverted, and alongside it, a unit matrix of the same size, numbering the rows and columns:

$$\begin{array}{c} 1 \\ 2 \\ 3 \end{array} \begin{bmatrix} 2 & 3 & -1 \\ 1 & -4 & 2 \\ 0 & -2 & 3 \end{bmatrix} \begin{bmatrix} 1 & 0 & 0 \\ 0 & 1 & 0 \\ 0 & 0 & 1 \end{bmatrix}$$
$$\quad\quad 1 \quad\ 2 \quad\ 3$$

(ii) Inspect the matrix, and find its numerically largest element. In this case it is -4, the second element of the second row.

(iii) By the interchange of rows, bring the row containing this largest element to the position of first row:

$$\begin{array}{c} 2 \\ 1 \\ 3 \end{array} \begin{bmatrix} 1 & -4 & 2 \\ 2 & 3 & -1 \\ 0 & -2 & 3 \end{bmatrix} \begin{bmatrix} 0 & 1 & 0 \\ 1 & 0 & 0 \\ 0 & 0 & 1 \end{bmatrix}$$
$$\quad\quad 1 \quad\ 2 \quad\ 3$$

Then, by the interchange of columns, bring this largest element to the leading position, that is to the first position in the first row and first column, keeping a record of the interchanged rows and columns in our extra row and column as shown below:

$$\begin{array}{c} 2 \\ 1 \\ 3 \end{array} \begin{bmatrix} -4 & 1 & 2 \\ 3 & 2 & -1 \\ -2 & 0 & 3 \end{bmatrix} \begin{bmatrix} 1 & 0 & 0 \\ 0 & 1 & 0 \\ 0 & 0 & 1 \end{bmatrix}$$
$$\quad\quad 2 \quad\ 1 \quad\ 3$$

(iv) Divide every element in the first row of both matrices by the element in the first column:

$$
\begin{matrix} 2 \\ 1 \\ 3 \end{matrix}
\begin{bmatrix} 1 & -1/4 & -1/2 \\ 3 & 2 & -1 \\ -2 & 0 & 3 \end{bmatrix}
\begin{bmatrix} -1/4 & 0 & 0 \\ 0 & 1 & 0 \\ 0 & 0 & 1 \end{bmatrix} .
$$
$$
 \begin{matrix} 2 & 1 & 3 \end{matrix}
$$

That is, in the double suffix notation, $a_{1j} \to a_{1j}/a_{11}$ and $b_{1j} \to b_{1j}/a_{11}$ for $j = 1,2,3$.

(v) Subtract the first row multiplied by the first element in the second row from the second row:

$$
\begin{matrix} 2 \\ 1 \\ 3 \end{matrix}
\begin{bmatrix} 1 & -1/4 & -1/2 \\ 0 & 11/4 & 1/2 \\ -2 & 0 & 3 \end{bmatrix}
\begin{bmatrix} -1/4 & 0 & 0 \\ 3/4 & 1 & 0 \\ 0 & 0 & 1 \end{bmatrix} .
$$
$$
 \begin{matrix} 2 & 1 & 3 \end{matrix}
$$

That is, $a_{2j} \to -a_{1j}a_{21} + a_{2j}$, $b_{2j} \to -b_{1j}a_{21} + b_{2j}$, for $j = 1,2,3$.

(vi) Subtract the first row, multiplied by the first element in the third row, from the third row:

$$
\begin{matrix} 2 \\ 1 \\ 3 \end{matrix}
\begin{bmatrix} 1 & -1/4 & -1/2 \\ 0 & 11/4 & 1/2 \\ 0 & -1/2 & 2 \end{bmatrix}
\begin{bmatrix} -1/4 & 0 & 0 \\ 3/4 & 1 & 0 \\ -1/2 & 0 & 1 \end{bmatrix} .
$$
$$
 \begin{matrix} 2 & 1 & 3 \end{matrix}
$$

The algorithm here is $a_{3j} \to -a_{1j}a_{31} + a_{3j}$ and $b_{3j} \to -b_{1j}a_{31} + b_{3j}$ for $j = 1,2,3$.

(vii) Ignoring the first row and column of the first matrix, seek through the remaining 2×2 sub-matrix for its numerically largest element and bring this into the leading position, that is into the second place down the diagonal, recording the changed rows and columns as before. Here, in fact, $11/4$ is already in the correct position.

(viii) Divide the first row of the sub-matrix by this largest element $11/4$ to obtain a 1 (one) on the diagonal position:

$$
\begin{matrix} 2 \\ 1 \\ 3 \end{matrix}
\begin{bmatrix} 1 & -1/4 & -1/2 \\ 0 & 1 & 2/11 \\ 0 & -1/2 & 2 \end{bmatrix}
\begin{bmatrix} -1/4 & 0 & 0 \\ 3/11 & 4/11 & 0 \\ -1/2 & 0 & 1 \end{bmatrix}
$$
$$
 \begin{matrix} 2 & 1 & 3 \end{matrix}
$$

That is, $a_{2j} \to a_{2j}/a_{22}$, for $j = 2,3$ and $b_{2j} \to b_{2j}/a_{22}$ for $j = 1,2,3$.

(ix) Subtract the second row multiplied by the second element in the third row from the third row:

$$\begin{array}{c} 2 \\ 1 \\ 3 \end{array} \begin{bmatrix} 1 & -1/4 & -1/2 \\ 0 & 1 & 2/11 \\ 0 & 0 & 23/11 \end{bmatrix} \begin{bmatrix} -1/4 & 0 & 0 \\ 3/11 & 4/11 & 0 \\ -4/11 & 2/11 & 1 \end{bmatrix}$$
$$ 2 \qquad 1 \qquad 3$$

The algorithm here is $a_{3j} \to -a_{2j}a_{32} + a_{3j}$, for $j = 2,3$ and $b_{3j} \to -b_{2j}a_{31} + b_{3j}$ for $j = 1,2,3$.

(x) Divide the third row by the element on its diagonal, $23/11$.

$$\begin{array}{c} 2 \\ 1 \\ 3 \end{array} \begin{bmatrix} 1 & -1/4 & -1/2 \\ 0 & 1 & 2/11 \\ 0 & 0 & 1 \end{bmatrix} \begin{bmatrix} -1/4 & 0 & 0 \\ 3/11 & 4/11 & 0 \\ -4/23 & 2/23 & 11/23 \end{bmatrix}$$
$$ 2 \qquad 1 \qquad 3$$

That is $a_{3j} \to a_{3j}/a_{33}$ for $j = 3$ and $b_{3j} \to b_{3j}/a_{33}$, for $j = 1,2,3$.

This completes the process of triangulation. At this point in the computation, the first matrix should have 1's down its diagonal and 0's below the diagonal. The matrix which is going to become the inverse, should have 0's above the diagonal. We now start the second stage of the calculation, called the back-substitution stage.

(xi) Subtract the last row, multiplied by the last element of the second row, $2/11$, from the second row, beyond the diagonal in the first matrix and all across in the second matrix:

$$\begin{array}{c} 2 \\ 1 \\ 3 \end{array} \begin{bmatrix} 1 & -1/4 & -1/2 \\ 0 & 1 & 0 \\ 0 & 0 & 1 \end{bmatrix} \begin{bmatrix} -1/4 & 0 & 0 \\ 7/23 & 8/23 & -2/23 \\ -4/23 & 2/23 & 11/23 \end{bmatrix}$$
$$ 2 \qquad 1 \qquad 3$$

Here $a_{2j} \to -a_{3j}a_{23} + a_{2j}$ for $j = 3$, and $b_{2j} \to -b_{3j}a_{23} + b_{2j}$ for $j = 1,2,3$.

(xii) Subtract the last row multiplied by the last element of the first row $(-1/2)$ from the first row, in the last column in the first matrix, and all across in the second matrix:

$$\begin{array}{c} 2 \\ 1 \\ 3 \end{array} \begin{bmatrix} 1 & -1/4 & 0 \\ 0 & 1 & 0 \\ 0 & 0 & 1 \end{bmatrix} \begin{bmatrix} -31/92 & 1/23 & 11/46 \\ 7/23 & 8/23 & -2/23 \\ -4/23 & 2/23 & 11/23 \end{bmatrix}$$
$$ 2 \qquad 1 \qquad 3$$

We have now produced a column of zeros in the last column of the first matrix. Here $a_{1j} \to -a_{3j}a_{13} + a_{1j}$ for $j = 3$ and $b_{1j} \to -b_{3j}a_{13} + b_{1j}$ for $j = 1,2,3$.

(xiii) Ignoring the last row and column of the first matrix, subtract the second row, multiplied by the second element of the first row, from the first row, beyond the diagonal in the first matrix, and all across in the second matrix:

$$
\begin{array}{c}
2 \\
1 \\
3
\end{array}
\begin{bmatrix}
1 & 0 & 0 \\
0 & 1 & 0 \\
0 & 0 & 1
\end{bmatrix}
\begin{bmatrix}
-6/23 & 3/23 & 5/23 \\
7/23 & 8/23 & -2/23 \\
-4/23 & 2/23 & 11/23
\end{bmatrix} .
$$
$$
\begin{array}{ccc}
2 & 1 & 3
\end{array}
$$

Here $a_{1j} \rightarrow -a_{2j}a_{12} + a_{1j}$ for $j = 2$, and $b_{1j} \rightarrow -b_{2j}a_{12} + b_{1j}$ for $j = 1,2,3$.

(xiv) Finally replace the rows in their correct order and replace the columns in their correct order:

$$
\begin{array}{c}
1 \\
2 \\
3
\end{array}
\begin{bmatrix}
1 & 0 & 0 \\
0 & 1 & 0 \\
0 & 0 & 1
\end{bmatrix}
\begin{bmatrix}
8/23 & 7/23 & -2/23 \\
3/23 & -6/23 & 5/23 \\
2/23 & -4/23 & 11/23
\end{bmatrix}
$$
$$
\begin{array}{ccc}
1 & 2 & 3
\end{array}
$$

We should now have the unit matrix I on the left and the required inverse A^{-1} on the right.

(xv) Check that the result is correct by multiplication

$$
\begin{bmatrix}
2 & 3 & -1 \\
1 & -4 & 2 \\
0 & -2 & 3
\end{bmatrix}
\times
\begin{bmatrix}
8/23 & 7/23 & -2/23 \\
3/23 & -6/23 & 5/23 \\
2/23 & -4/23 & 11/23
\end{bmatrix}
=
\begin{bmatrix}
1 & 0 & 0 \\
0 & 1 & 0 \\
0 & 0 & 1
\end{bmatrix} ,
$$

that is $A \times A^{-1} = I$.

Every method of inverting a matrix involves a repeated subtraction and division process. Unless we guard against it in every possible way, we are faced with an increasing loss of significant figures in our calculation and perhaps even an implicit division by a near-zero quantity may arise. It is in order to guard against such zero divisions, that we start each cycle of the calculation by dividing by the largest element present. If then near-zero division still occurs, the matrix is said to be singular, that is abnormal in the sense that every element in one row is a constant multiple or some other simple function of every element in another row. Trying to invert a singular matrix is similar to trying to form $1/0$ in ordinary scalars. It can be shown that the loss of significant figures is minimised by the process of subtracting and back-substitution adopted here, and, as we shall see below, the process is readily generalised to one for the inversion of matrices of quite large order. A matrix in which all the elements of a row or column are zeros is always singular.

§1.4 Inversion of high order matrices

The inversion of any matrix is a complicated process, and the number of steps involved increases very quickly as the size of the matrix increases. Thus, we need about $4 \times 3^3 + 4 \times 2^3 = 140$ operations to invert a 3×3 matrix, but we need about $4 \times 4^3 + 4 \times 3^3 + 4 \times 2^3 = 396$ operations to invert a 4×4 matrix. At each increase of one in the size, n, of the matrix, the number of numerical operations required to produce an inverse increases by about $4n^3$, so that in general we need to carry out about

19

$$4(1^3 + 2^3 + \dots + n^3) = 4\sum_{v=1}^{n} v^3 = n^2(n+1)^2 \qquad (1.4.1)$$

operations in order to invert an $n \times n$ matrix.

This really means that for $n \geqslant 5$, we have to use an electronic computer. The best method of inversion is that which

(i) Preserves the greatest accuracy,

(ii) Avoids division by small elements or subtraction of nearly equal elements,

(iii) Uses as little storage space as possible,

(iv) Gives a cyclic, repetitive process of solution which can be programmed fairly easily.

The process which is most widely used, and which is used in the present program, is that of triangulation and back-substitution outlined above. First we mark out a unit matrix in the store alongside the matrix to be inverted:

$$A = \begin{bmatrix} a_{11} & a_{12} & \dots \\ a_{21} & a_{22} & \dots \\ & \dots & \end{bmatrix} \qquad B = \begin{bmatrix} 1 & 0 & \dots \\ 0 & 1 & \dots \\ & \dots & \end{bmatrix}.$$

Each matrix has $N \times N$ elements. We check that $N > 1$, that is that the matrix is not just a scalar. Then we seek through the matrix A to find its largest element. Let this be in row p. We bring this row up to the head of the matrix by interchanging rows in both the matrix and its inverse. We check that the element on the diagonal a_{11} is not very small. Then we divide throughout the whole first row of both the matrix and its inverse by a_{11}, and we replace the diagonal element itself by an exact 1 (one). Our stored matrices are now

$$\begin{bmatrix} 1 & a_{12}/a_{11} & \dots \\ a_{21} & a_{22} & \dots \\ & \dots & \end{bmatrix} \begin{bmatrix} 1/a_{11} & 0 & 0 & \dots \\ 0 & 1 & 0 & \dots \\ & & \dots & \end{bmatrix}.$$

We form $\{(-a_{21}) \times$ 1st row + 2nd row$\}$ of both the matrix and the inverse. This gives a 0 (nought) in the first place of the second row.

That is

$$a_{2j} \rightarrow -a_{21}a_{1j}/a_{11} + a_{2j}$$

and $\qquad b_{2j} \rightarrow -b_{21}b_{1j}/a_{11} + b_{2j} \qquad$ for $j = 1, 2, 3, \dots, N.$ $\qquad (1.4.2)$

We repeat this process down the first column, finishing with $\{1 \quad 0 \quad 0 \quad \dots\}$ down this column. The general statement is now

$$a_{ij} \rightarrow -a_{i1}a_{1j}/a_{11} + a_{ij}$$

and $\qquad b_{ij} \rightarrow -b_{i1}b_{1j}/a_{11} + b_{ij} \qquad$ for $\quad i = 1, 2, 3, \dots, N$ $\qquad (1.4.3)$

$$\text{and} \quad j = 1, 2, 3, \dots, N.$$

Then we seek the largest element in the remaining sub-matrix formed by

20

omitting the first row and column of the matrix A. We bring the row containing this element to the position of second row, and divide the whole second row of the matrix and inverse by the element now on the diagonal position.

Then we form $\{(-a_{32}) \times$ 2nd row $+$ 3rd row$\}$ across the third row of both matrices to get a 0 (nought) in the second place of the third row. We repeat the whole process down the second column. That is

$$a_{ij} \rightarrow -a_{i2}a_{2j}/a_{22} + a_{ij}$$

and
$$b_{ij} \rightarrow -b_{i2}b_{2j}/a_{22} + b_{ij} \quad \text{for} \quad i = 3, 4, ..., N \tag{1.4.4}$$

$$\text{and} \quad j = 1, 2, 3, ..., N.$$

This process continues until we have exhausted all the rows. We have now triangulated the A matrix, and it looks like this:—

$$\begin{bmatrix} 1 & a_{12} & a_{13} & \cdots \\ 0 & 1 & a_{23} & \cdots \\ 0 & 0 & 1 & \cdots \\ & & \cdots & \end{bmatrix},$$

with 1's down the main diagonal and 0's underneath.

The general form of the algorithm used here is now revealed to be

$$a_{ij} \rightarrow a_{ij} - a_{ik}a_{kj}/a_{kk} \quad \text{in the } A \text{ matrix}$$

and
$$b_{ij} \rightarrow b_{ij} - b_{ik}b_{kj}/a_{kk} \quad \text{in the } B \text{ matrix} \tag{1.4.5}$$

for $\quad i = k+1, k+2, ..., N, \quad k = 1, 2, 3, ..., N \quad$ and $\quad j = 1, 2, 3, ..., N.$

Now we start the second stage of the calculation, the back substitution. We subtract the element in the last column of the A matrix times the elements in the last but one row of the B matrix from the corresponding elements in the last but one row of the inverse matrix B. The algorithm here is

$$b_{ij} \rightarrow b_{ij} - a_{ik}b_{kj} \quad \text{for} \quad i = N-k, N-k-1, ..., 2,$$

$$j = 1, 2, ..., N, \quad \text{and} \quad k = N, N-1, N-2, ..., 2. \tag{1.4.6}$$

Here we have repeated the above process, with the last element of every row of the A matrix, making the last column of the A matrix $\{0 \quad 0 \quad \cdots \quad 0 \quad 1\}$. Then we have repeated the whole of the process with the elements of the sub-matrix formed by ignoring the last row and column of the A matrix. This gives a last but one column in the A matrix of the form $\{0 \quad 0 \quad \cdots \quad 0 \quad 1 \quad 0\}$.

We repeat the process with each possible sub-matrix of A formed by dropping the last rows and columns, and operating every time on the B matrix as well. Finally our A matrix becomes a unit matrix and the original unit matrix becomes the required inverse B. The above example on a 3×3 matrix should make every step in the process clear.

SECTION 2

A GENERAL MATRIX PROGRAM

§1.5 Specification

This program reads in a data tape which consists of matrices, diagonal matrices, vectors, constants and control digits. It performs simple arithmetic operations on these items according to the values of the control digits. All the matrices are punched in row order, on paper tape. Each matrix is headed by an identification punched as a real number, and the number of rows, m, and the number of items per row, n, punched as integers. These three items must be on one line, but the format used here is a free one, so that provided that those numbers which have to be integers are punched as integers, that is with no decimal points, and that each item is followed by at least one space, the actual detail of the format is left open. If a fixed format is desired, the items labelled 1 and 801 would have to be changed as required. Also if card input is preferred to tape input, only these two format statements need to be altered.

Diagonal matrices and row or column vectors are punched in a similar free format, as single rows or columns, each headed by its identifying number, and m the number of its elements. Constants are punched as real numbers, also in free format. Control digits are punched as integers, and each control digit must be on a line by itself.

The name of the program, by which it is known to the computer, is MM1A. The storage space required for this version is about 12000, but this depends to some extent on the efficiency of the Fortran compiler in use in the computing system. The program requires one input channel, which here is a paper tape reader, but this can easily be changed for a card reader as remarked above. It also requires one output channel, which can be either a tape punch or a line printer. It does not use any magnetic tape units for background storage of data.

The main matrix sequence is of size $m \times n$ where m and n are both less than 36. The control digits provided are all integers, running from -2 up to 19. They have the following effects:

-2 Pause at the end of a data tape.

-1 Clear the main matrix sequence to zeros. This must always be done at the start of each separate calculation.

 0 Read a matrix in rows and add the matrix being read to the matrix already in the store.

 1 Read a matrix in rows and subtract the matrix being read from the matrix already in the matrix store.

 2 Read a matrix in rows and pre-multiply the matrix in the matrix store by the matrix being read.

 3 Read a matrix in rows and post-multiply the matrix in the matrix store by the matrix being read.

 4 Replace the matrix in the matrix store by its inverse.

5   Read a vector and pre-multiply the matrix in the matrix store by this vector.

6   Read a vector and post-multiply the matrix in the matrix store by this vector.
    Note: digits 5 and 6 do not alter the matrix in the matrix store, but put the resultant vector into another sequence ready to be printed as a vector.

7   Read a diagonal matrix and pre-multiply the matrix in the matrix store by this diagonal matrix.

8   Read a diagonal matrix and post-multiply the matrix in the matrix store by this diagonal matrix.

9   Print the matrix in the matrix store in rows, with its correct heading.
    Note: if tape output is used this matrix is in a form ready for re-input in later calculations.

10 Print a vector, a diagonal matrix or a single item from the vector store, with its correct heading, ready for re-input.

11 Read a vector and multiply the vector in the store by this vector, to give a scalar quantity.

12 Read a decimal constant and multiply the matrix in the matrix store by this constant.

13 Read a decimal constant and multiply the vector in the vector store by this constant.

14 Transpose the matrix in the matrix store.

15 Add a unit matrix to the matrix in the matrix store.

16 Divide the matrix in the matrix store by the sums along its rows. These sums are left in the vector store ready to be printed if required.

17 Divide the matrix in the matrix store by the sums down its columns. Again the sums are left ready for printing, in the vector store.

18 Form and print the sum of all the elements of the matrix.

19 Form the Kth power of the matrix in the matrix store.

The structure of the program is such that further control digits can be added at this point, if space is available in the computer. Also, by altering the size of the common sequences A, B, C and D, the size of the largest matrix, which can be input, can be increased if more space is available, or decreased if it is desired to get the program into a smaller space. In both cases the line at label 9 must be altered also, but no other alterations are required in the program.

All printing is to five significant figures, in full floating point notation. Again only some format statements need to be changed if another form of output is desired. Tape output is in a form ready for re-input with a string of 30 space symbols separating each section of the output tape.

As an example, let us consider the data tape required to form $(I-A)^{-1}$, where the matrix A has the code number 8.1, and is of size 10×10.

−1   Clear the matrix store to zeros.

1   Code numbers of matrix A.

			Read in A in rows and subtract from

8.1   10   10   Read in A in rows and subtract from

a_{11} a_{12} ... $a_{1\ 10}$ the zero matrix leaving $-A$ in store.

a_{21} a_{22} ... $a_{2\ 10}$ Output the identifying number of

...   the matrix A and each code digit as

$a_{10\ 1}$ $a_{10\ 2}$ ... $a_{10\ 10}$ it is obeyed.

15   Add the unit matrix of size 10×10

to the matrix $-A$ in store.

4   Invert $(I - A)$.

9   Output $(I - A)^{-1}$ with its correct

heading and terminating sequences,

ready for re-input if required.

−2   Stop the calculation and print

END OF DATA.

§1.6 Flow diagrams

The specification above told us what the program does, how to make intelligent use of the program, how to lay out the input data in the correct pattern and how to interpret the resulting output. It does not go into a detailed statement of the individual stages in the calculation. The program itself is a list of orders stored as electronic patterns in the memory of the computer. At any given moment in the computations, the computer can be thought of as obeying one of these orders at a particular point in the program. Control is the act of passing from obeying one order to obeying another order. Usually control passes in sequence from one order to the next one within the computer, but occasionally a logical choice has to be made in the calculations. A flow diagram is an aid to the understanding of the logical flow of the computer program.

The conventions used in this work are fairly standard. Square brackets [   ] enclose arithmetical statements. Round brackets (   ) enclose input or output activities. Angled brackets 〈   〉 enclose 'if' clauses, that is points at which a logical choice has to be made in the program. Numbers in round brackets (N) indicate joins between one part of the flow diagram and another part. Arrows →, ↑, ← or ↓ indicate the direction of the logical flow of the calculation. In an arithmetical statement, a dash ' indicates the new value of an item. Thus $a_2' = a_2 + b_2$ means that the new value of a_2, that is a_2', is equal to the old value of a_2 added to the value of b_2.

Program MM1A, flow diagrams for the master routine.

[Start]

↓

(Runout 30 spaces on paper tape)

↓

(Write heading 'MATRIX PROGRAM MM1A')

↓

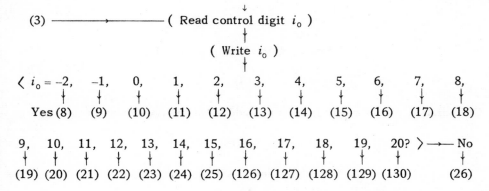

(3) ──────────── (Read control digit i_o)

(Write i_o)

$\langle\; i_o = -2,\quad -1,\quad 0,\quad 1,\quad 2,\quad 3,\quad 4,\quad 5,\quad 6,\quad 7,\quad 8,$

Yes (8) (9) (10) (11) (12) (13) (14) (15) (16) (17) (18)

9, 10, 11, 12, 13, 14, 15, 16, 17, 18, 19, 20? $\rangle$ ── No

(19) (20) (21) (22) (23) (24) (25) (126) (127) (128) (129) (130)   (26)

This is a multiway switch. It switches control to different points in the program as labelled, according to the value of i_o. If i_o is not equal to any of the permitted control digits, read and ignore the faulty data up to the next -1 digit.

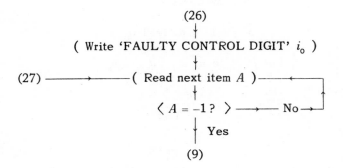

(26)

(Write 'FAULTY CONTROL DIGIT' i_o)

(27) ──────── (Read next item A)────←

$\langle\; A = -1\,? \;\rangle$ ──── No →

Yes

(9)

Code digit -2, pause at end of run.

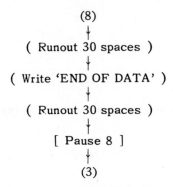

(8)

(Runout 30 spaces)

(Write 'END OF DATA')

(Runout 30 spaces)

[Pause 8]

(3)

Pause 8 is the normal end for a correct calculation.
Code digit -1, clear working sequences to zeros.

$$(9)$$
$$\downarrow$$
$$[\ \text{For}\ i = 1\ \text{to}\ 1296,\ a_i = b_i = 0\ ]$$
$$\downarrow$$
$$(3)$$

Code digit 0, read a matrix in rows and add to the matrix already in the store.

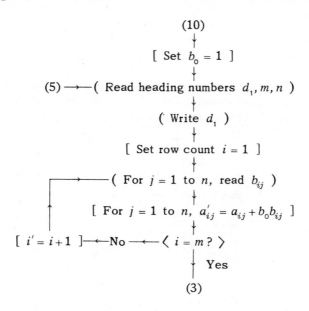

$$(10)$$
$$\downarrow$$
$$[\ \text{Set}\ b_0 = 1\ ]$$
$$\downarrow$$

$(5) \longrightarrow$ (Read heading numbers d_1, m, n)

$$\downarrow$$

(Write d_1)

$$\downarrow$$

[Set row count $i = 1$]

$$\downarrow$$

(For $j = 1$ to n, read b_{ij})

$$\downarrow$$

[For $j = 1$ to n, $a'_{ij} = a_{ij} + b_0 b_{ij}$]

$$\downarrow$$

$[\ i' = i+1\ ] \longleftarrow \text{No} \longleftarrow \langle\ i = m\ ?\ \rangle$

$$\downarrow\ \text{Yes}$$

$$(3)$$

Code digit 1, read a matrix in rows and subtract from the matrix already in the store, that is set $b_0 = -1$, and use the previous routine.

$$(11)$$
$$\downarrow$$
$$[\ b_0 = -1\ ]$$
$$\downarrow$$
$$(5)$$

Code digit 2, read a matrix in rows and pre-multiply the matrix in the store by the matrix being read.

$$(12)$$
$$\downarrow$$

(Read heading d_1, m_1, n_1)

$$\downarrow$$

(Write d_1)

$$\downarrow$$

$\langle\ n_1 = m\ ?\ \rangle \longrightarrow \text{No, faulty data} \longrightarrow (26)$

$$\downarrow\ \text{Yes}$$
$$\downarrow$$

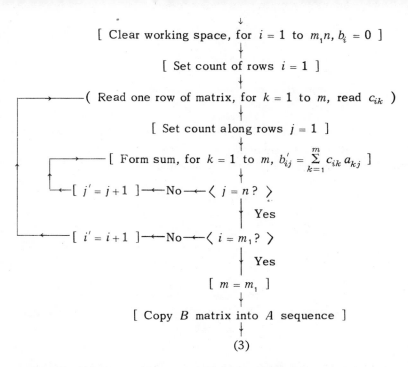

[Clear working space, for $i = 1$ to $m_1 n$, $b_i = 0$]

[Set count of rows $i = 1$]

(Read one row of matrix, for $k = 1$ to m, read c_{ik})

[Set count along rows $j = 1$]

[Form sum, for $k = 1$ to m, $b'_{ij} = \sum_{k=1}^{m} c_{ik} a_{kj}$]

←[$j' = j+1$]——No——< $j = n$? >

Yes

——[$i' = i+1$]——No——< $i = m_1$? >

Yes

[$m = m_1$]

[Copy B matrix into A sequence]

(3)

Code digit 3, read a matrix in rows and post-multiply the matrix in the store by the matrix being read.

(13)

(Read heading d_1, m_1, n_1)

(Write d_1)

< $m_1 = n$? > —— No, faulty data ——(26)

Yes

[Clear working space, for $i = 1$ to mn_1, $b_i = 0$]

[Set row count of input matrix, $k = 1$]

(Read one row of matrix, for $j = 1$ to n_1, read c_{kj})

[Set count over rows of B matrix, $i = 1$]

——[For $j = 1$ to n_1, $b'_{ij} = b_{ij} + a_{ik} c_{kj}$]

[$i' = i+1$]—— No —— < $i = m$? >

Yes

——[$k' = k+1$]—— No —— < $k = n$? >

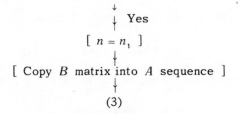

$$\downarrow \text{Yes}$$

$$[\ n = n_1\ ]$$

$$\downarrow$$

$$[\ \text{Copy } B \text{ matrix into } A \text{ sequence }\ ]$$

$$\downarrow$$

$$(3)$$

Code digit 4, invert matrix in A sequence.
Set up unit matrix in B sequence, and check that matrix is square.

$$(14)$$

$$\downarrow$$

$$[\ \text{For } i = 1 \text{ to } mn,\ b_i = 0\ ]$$

$$\downarrow$$

$$[\ \text{For } i = 1 \text{ by } n+1 \text{ to } mn,\ b_i = 1\ ]$$

$$\downarrow$$

$$\langle\ m = n\,?\ \rangle \longrightarrow \text{No} \longrightarrow (\ \text{Write 'MATRIX NOT}$$

$$\downarrow \text{Yes} \qquad\qquad \text{SQUARE' } d_1\ )$$

$$(995) \qquad\qquad\qquad (3)$$

Set j count for main cycle along rows, seek largest element down jth column,
from the diagonal downwards, set $x = $ largest element and set $i = $ number of row
containing this largest element.

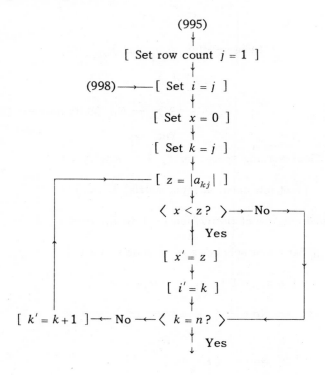

$$(995)$$

$$\downarrow$$

$$[\ \text{Set row count } j = 1\ ]$$

$$\downarrow$$

$$(998) \longrightarrow [\ \text{Set } i = j\ ]$$

$$\downarrow$$

$$[\ \text{Set } x = 0\ ]$$

$$\downarrow$$

$$[\ \text{Set } k = j\ ]$$

$$\downarrow$$

$$[\ z = |a_{kj}|\ ]$$

$$\downarrow$$

$$\langle\ x < z\,?\ \rangle \longrightarrow \text{No} \longrightarrow$$

$$\downarrow \text{Yes}$$

$$[\ x' = z\ ]$$

$$\downarrow$$

$$[\ i' = k\ ]$$

$$\downarrow$$

$$[\ k' = k+1\ ] \longleftarrow \text{No} \longleftarrow \langle\ k = n\,?\ \rangle$$

$$\downarrow \text{Yes}$$

$$\downarrow$$

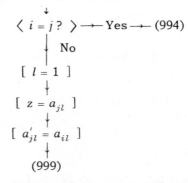

$$\langle\, i = j\, ? \,\rangle \longrightarrow \text{Yes} \longrightarrow (994)$$

$$\downarrow \ \text{No}$$

$$[\ l = 1\ ]$$

$$\downarrow$$

$$[\ z = a_{jl}\ ]$$

$$\downarrow$$

$$[\ a'_{jl} = a_{il}\ ]$$

$$\downarrow$$

$$(999)$$

If the largest element is already on the first row, skip to next section, otherwise interchange all the elements in row j and row i in both the A and B matrices.

$$(999)$$

$$\downarrow$$

$$[\ a'_{il} = z\ ]$$

$$\downarrow$$

$$[\ y = b_{jl}\ ]$$

$$\downarrow$$

$$[\ b'_{jl} = b_{il}\ ]$$

$$\downarrow$$

$$[\ b'_{il} = y\ ]$$

$$\downarrow$$

$$(994)$$

Test if the matrix is nearly singular. If it is not, transform the upper triangle of the A matrix and all of the B matrix according to the algorithms.

$$(994)$$

$$\downarrow$$

$$\langle\, |a_{jj}| \leqslant 10^{-8}? \,\rangle \longrightarrow \text{Yes} \longrightarrow (\text{ Write 'ZERO PIVOT'}\ d_1\ )$$

$$\downarrow \ \text{No} \qquad\qquad\qquad \downarrow$$

$$[\ a_0 = 1/a_{jj}\ ] \qquad\qquad (3)$$

$$[\ \text{For } l = j+1 \text{ to } n,\ a'_{jl} = a_0 a_{jl}\ ]$$

$$[\ \text{For } l = 1 \text{ to } n,\ b'_{jl} = a_0 b_{jl}\ ]$$

$$[\ a_{jj} = 1\ ]$$

$$[\ k = j+1\ ]$$

$$[\ \text{For } l = j+1 \text{ to } n,\ a'_{kl} = a_{kl} - a_{kj} a_{jl}\ ]$$

$$[\ \text{For } l = 1 \text{ to } n,\ b'_{kl} = b_{kl} - a_{kj} b_{jl}\ ]$$

$$\downarrow$$

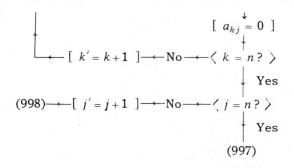

$$[\ a_{kj} = 0\ ]$$

$\longleftarrow$ [$k' = k+1$] $\longleftarrow$ No $\longleftarrow$ ⟨ $k = n$? ⟩

$\quad$ Yes

(998) $\longleftarrow$ [$j' = j+1$] $\longleftarrow$ No $\longleftarrow$ ⟨ $j = n$? ⟩

$\quad$ Yes

(997)

Carry out back-substitution over the B matrix.

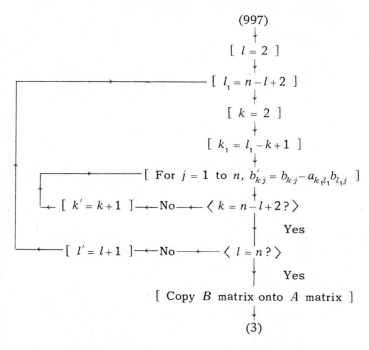

(997)

$$[\ l = 2\ ]$$

$$[\ l_1 = n - l + 2\ ]$$

$$[\ k = 2\ ]$$

$$[\ k_1 = l_1 - k + 1\ ]$$

[For $j = 1$ to n, $b'_{kj} = b_{kj} - a_{k_1 l_1} b_{l_1 j}$]

$\longleftarrow$ [$k' = k+1$] $\longleftarrow$ No $\longleftarrow$ ⟨ $k = n - l + 2$? ⟩

$\quad$ Yes

$\longleftarrow$ [$l' = l+1$] $\longleftarrow$ No $\longleftarrow$ ⟨ $l = n$? ⟩

$\quad$ Yes

[Copy B matrix onto A matrix]

(3)

Code digit 5, read a vector and pre-multiply the matrix in the matrix store by this vector.

(15)

(Read heading d_1, m_1)

(Write d_1)

⟨ $m_1 = m$? ⟩ $\longrightarrow$ No $\longrightarrow$ (Write 'FAULTY VECTOR' d_1')

$\quad$ Yes

(For $i = 1$ to m, read d_i)

(27)

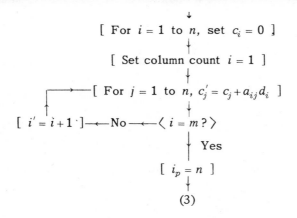

$$\downarrow$$

[For $i = 1$ to n, set $c_i = 0$]

$$\downarrow$$

[Set column count $i = 1$]

$$\downarrow$$

──────[For $j = 1$ to n, $c_j' = c_j + a_{ij}d_i$]

[$i' = i+1$]──No──⟨ $i = m$? ⟩

Yes

[$i_p = n$]

(3)

Code digit 6, read a vector and post-multiply the matrix in the matrix store by this vector.

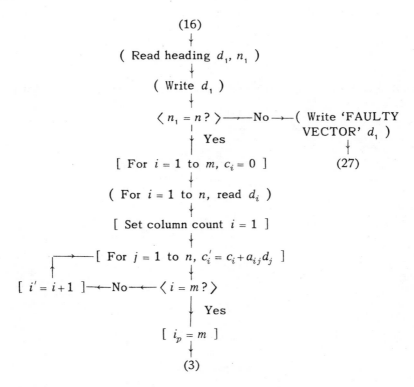

(16)

$$\downarrow$$

(Read heading d_1, n_1)

$$\downarrow$$

(Write d_1)

$$\downarrow$$

⟨ $n_1 = n$? ⟩────No──(Write 'FAULTY VECTOR' d_1)

Yes

[For $i = 1$ to m, $c_i = 0$]   (27)

$$\downarrow$$

(For $i = 1$ to n, read d_i)

$$\downarrow$$

[Set column count $i = 1$]

$$\downarrow$$

──────[For $j = 1$ to n, $c_i' = c_i + a_{ij}d_j$]

[$i' = i+1$]──No──⟨ $i = m$? ⟩

Yes

[$i_p = m$]

(3)

Note: i_p is the number of items in the vector to be printed if the 'print vector' routine is entered next.

Digit 7, read a diagonal matrix and pre-multiply the matrix in the matrix store by this diagonal matrix.

(17)

$$\downarrow$$

(Read heading d_1, m_1)

31

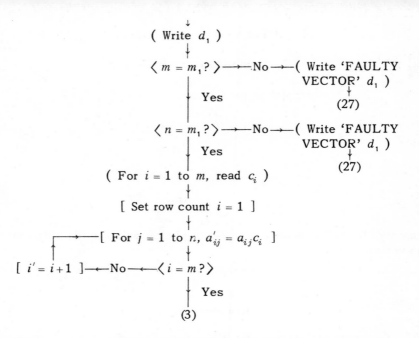

Digit 8, read a diagonal matrix and post-multiply the matrix in the matrix store by this diagonal matrix.

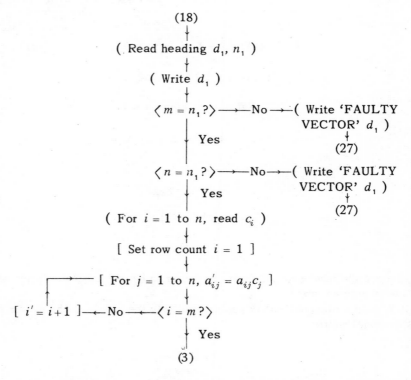

Digit 9, print the matrix in the store in rows, in the correct form ready for re-input.

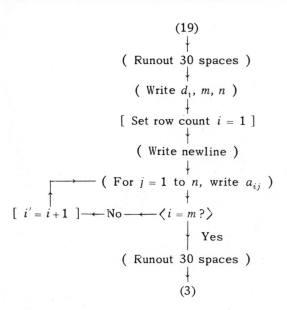

(19)

(Runout 30 spaces)

(Write d_1, m, n)

[Set row count $i = 1$]

(Write newline)

(For $j = 1$ to n, write a_{ij})

[$i' = i + 1$] ←— No ←— $\langle i = m ? \rangle$

Yes

(Runout 30 spaces)

(3)

Digit 10, print a vector or a diagonal matrix from the vector sequence, in the correct form suitable for re-input.

(20)

(Runout 30 spaces)

(Write heading d_1, i_p)

(For $i = 1$ to i_p, write c_i)

(Runout 30 spaces)

(3)

Digit 11, read a vector and multiply the vector in the store by this vector.

(21)

(Read heading d_1, n_1)

(For $i = 1$ to n_1, read d_i)

[For $i = 1$ to n_1, $x = \sum_{i=1}^{n_1} c_i d_i$]

[$c_1 = x$]

(3)

c

Digit 12, read a decimal constant and multiply the matrix in the matrix store by this constant.

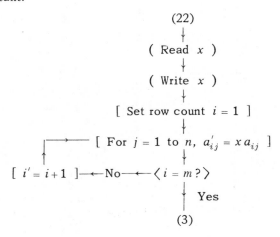

$$(22)$$
$$\downarrow$$
$$(\ \text{Read}\ \ x\ )$$
$$\downarrow$$
$$(\ \text{Write}\ \ x\ )$$
$$\downarrow$$
$$[\ \text{Set row count}\ \ i = 1\ ]$$
$$\downarrow$$
$$[\ \text{For}\ j = 1\ \text{to}\ n,\ a'_{ij} = x\,a_{ij}\ ]$$
$$[\ i' = i+1\ ] \longleftarrow \text{No} \longleftarrow \langle\, i = m\,? \,\rangle$$
$$\downarrow\ \text{Yes}$$
$$(3)$$

Digit 13, read a decimal constant and multiply the vector in the store by this constant.

$$(23)$$
$$\downarrow$$
$$(\ \text{Read}\ \ x\ )$$
$$\downarrow$$
$$(\ \text{Write}\ \ x\ )$$
$$\downarrow$$
$$[\ \text{For}\ i = 1\ \text{to}\ i_p,\ c'_i = x\,c_i\ ]$$
$$\downarrow$$
$$(3)$$

Digit 14, transpose the matrix in the matrix store.

$$(24)$$
$$\downarrow$$
$$[\ \text{Set first count}\ \ i = 1\ ]$$
$$\downarrow$$
$$[\ \text{For}\ j = 1\ \text{to}\ n,\ b_{ji} = a_{ij}\ ]$$
$$[\ i' = i+1\ ] \longleftarrow \text{No} \longleftarrow \langle\, i = m\,? \,\rangle$$
$$\downarrow\ \text{Yes}$$
$$[\ \text{Interchange}\ m\ \text{and}\ n\ ]$$
$$\downarrow$$
$$[\ i_p = n\ ]$$
$$\downarrow$$
$$[\ \text{Copy}\ B\ \text{sequence into}\ A\ \text{sequence}\ ]$$
$$\downarrow$$
$$(3)$$

Digit 15, add a unit matrix of size $m \times m$ to the main matrix store.

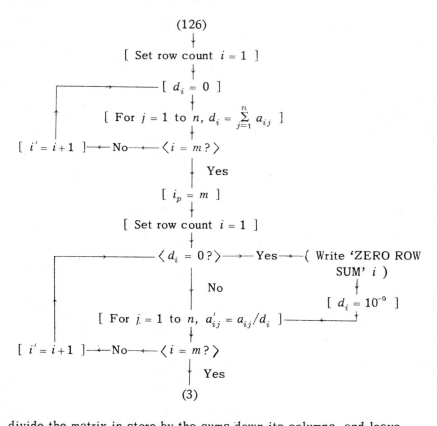

(25)
↓
[For $i = 1$ to m, $a'_{ii} = a_{ii} + 1$]
↓
(3)

Digit 16, divide the matrix in store by the sums along its rows, and leave these sums in the vector sequence ready to be printed.

(126)
↓
[Set row count $i = 1$]
↓
[$d_i = 0$]
↓
[For $j = 1$ to n, $d_i = \sum_{j=1}^{n} a_{ij}$]
↓
[$i' = i + 1$]—No—⟨ $i = m$? ⟩
↓ Yes
[$i_p = m$]
↓
[Set row count $i = 1$]
↓
⟨ $d_i = 0$? ⟩——Yes——(Write 'ZERO ROW SUM' i)
↓ No   ↓
                                [$d_i = 10^{-9}$]
[For $j = 1$ to n, $a'_{ij} = a_{ij}/d_i$]———
↓
[$i' = i + 1$]—No—⟨ $i = m$? ⟩
↓ Yes
(3)

Digit 17, divide the matrix in store by the sums down its columns, and leave these sums in the vector sequence ready to be printed.

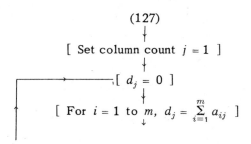

(127)
↓
[Set column count $j = 1$]
↓
[$d_j = 0$]
↓
[For $i = 1$ to m, $d_j = \sum_{i=1}^{m} a_{ij}$]
↓

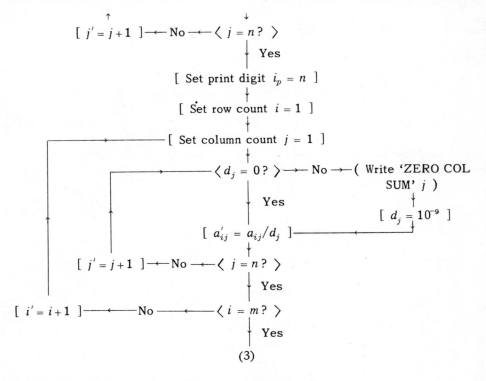

$[j' = j+1] \longleftarrow$ No $\longleftarrow \langle j = n? \rangle$

Yes

$[$ Set print digit $i_p = n]$

$[$ Set row count $i = 1]$

$[$ Set column count $j = 1]$

$\langle d_j = 0? \rangle \longrightarrow$ No $\longrightarrow ($ Write 'ZERO COL SUM' $j)$

Yes

$[d_j = 10^{-9}]$

$[a'_{ij} = a_{ij}/d_j]$

$[j' = j+1] \longleftarrow$ No $\longleftarrow \langle j = n? \rangle$

Yes

$[i' = i+1] \longleftarrow$ No $\longleftarrow \langle i = m? \rangle$

Yes

(3)

Digit 18, form the sum of all the elements of the matrix.

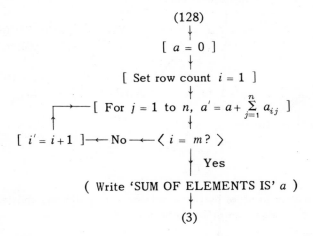

(128)

$[a = 0]$

$[$ Set row count $i = 1]$

$[$ For $j = 1$ to n, $a' = a + \sum_{j=1}^{n} a_{ij}]$

$[i' = i+1] \longleftarrow$ No $\longleftarrow \langle i = m? \rangle$

Yes

$($ Write 'SUM OF ELEMENTS IS' $a)$

(3)

Digit 19, form the Kth power of the matrix in the matrix store.

(129)

$($ Read $K)$

$($ Write $K)$

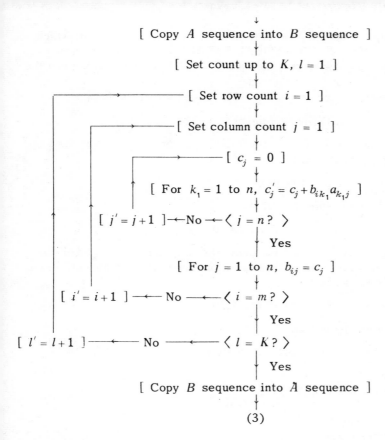

[Copy A sequence into B sequence]

[Set count up to K, $l = 1$]

[Set row count $i = 1$]

[Set column count $j = 1$]

[$c_j = 0$]

[For $k_1 = 1$ to n, $c'_j = c_j + b_{ik_1} a_{k_1 j}$]

[$j' = j+1$]—No—$\langle j = n ? \rangle$ Yes

[For $j = 1$ to n, $b_{ij} = c_j$]

[$i' = i+1$]—— No ——$\langle i = m ? \rangle$ Yes

[$l' = l+1$]—— No ——$\langle l = K ? \rangle$ Yes

[Copy B sequence into A sequence]

(3)

Digit 20, spare.

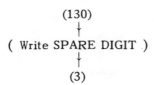

(130)

(Write SPARE DIGIT)

(3)

§1.7 The language of Fortran

The programming language used here is a very simple version of Fortran IV. The names of variables have from one to four letters and they are terminated by either an operating symbol or a space. Names starting with the letters I, J, K, L, M or N represent integer quantities in the range -1023 to $+1023$. Names starting with any other letter represent real decimal numbers in the range -10^{10} to $+10^{10}$.

The arithmetical operators are:

$+$ (addition), $-$ (subtraction), $*$ (multiplication),

$/$ (division)   and $**$ (exponentation).

37

The equality sign = occurs once only in each assigning statement, which then has the form NAME = ARITHMETICAL EXPRESSION. At the time that a statement of this type is carried out, the variable NAME on the left is given the numerical value of the quantity on the right.

Labels are integers in the range 1 to 999. Loops are of the form

$$\text{DO (label) Integer} = I_1, I_2, I_3$$

where I_1 is the starting value of I, I_2 its finishing value at the end of the loop, and I_3 the step size. For example,

$$\text{DO 40 I} = 2,20,2$$

would mean that I takes in turn the values

$$2,4,6, \ldots, 18,20,$$

in all the following orders up to and including the line starting with label 40. Loops can be nested within one-another up to four deep. If I_3 is absent, a step size of one is assumed, so that

$$\text{DO 40 I} = 2,20$$

would mean that I took the values

$$2,3,4, \ldots, 18,19,20$$

within the loop.

The simple switch order

$$\text{GO TO M}$$

sends control to the label M.

The multiple switch order

$$\text{GO TO } (L_1, L_2, \ldots, L_N) \text{ I}$$

where $L_1, L_2, \ldots$, are labels, sends control to L_1 when I = 1, to L_2, when I = 2, and so on.

The IF clause has the form

$$\text{IF (expression) } L_1, L_2, L_3$$

(where L_1, L_2, L_3 are labels). Control goes to L_1 if the expression is less than zero, control goes to L_2 if the expression equals zero and control goes to L_3 if the expression is greater than zero. Control goes on to the next statement in the program if any L = 0. There are no FUNCTION calls in the present programs.

Lines in the program which start with C in the first column, are lines of comment which are ignored completely by the compiler.

The arrays used here are all one dimensional, with an integer function as suffix. For example

$$A(1), A(2), \ldots, A(I*N + J - N).$$

They are declared in a COMMON / / statement at the head of the program.

The heading for a subroutine is

$$\text{SUBROUTINE NAME } (P_1, P_2, \ldots,)$$

COMMON / / List of common sequences.

The name of the subroutine must identify it uniquely. It can have from one to eight letters or integers. The parameters $P_1, P_2, ...,$ are the names given to those variables within the subroutine, which are calculated or used by the subroutine, but are not included in the list of COMMON sequences. A subroutine is entered at its first order and left at the order RETURN. A subroutine is called by the main program by the order

$$\text{CALL NAME } (P_1, P_2, ...),$$

where now the parameters $P_1, P_2, ...,$ and the items in the common sequences have the explicit values at the moment of entry to the subroutine. Control returns from the order RETURN in the subroutine to that order in the main program which follows the CALL order. The parameters $P_1, P_2, ...,$ and the common sequences have now the values at the moment of exit from the subroutine.

Input and output are by means of READ and WRITE statements respectively. Each channel of input or output is identified by a simple integer, in declarations at the head of the program, for example INPUT 1 = TR0. They are referred to by these integers throughout the program. The layout of the data is controlled in the usual way by FORMAT statements. The Format statements here only use /, E, F, I, and H layouts. / is for a newline on paper tape output, E and F are for floating point in input and output, and I is for integer data. H is for literal output of the symbols which follow it.

Two analytic built in subroutines are used: ABS for the absolute value, and SQRT for the squareroot.

Fuller information about the Fortran language will be found in D.D. McCracken's *Guide to Fortran Programming* (John Wiley, New York 1961), or in the various handbooks supplied by the computer manufacturers.

§1.8 Main Fortran program MM1A

```
PROGRAM (MM1A)
INPUT 1 = TR0
OUTPUT 2 = TP0
END


MASTER MM1A

C     MATRIX PACKAGE FOR GENERAL USE L. J.S. 6.7.66

COMMON / / A(1296), B(1296), C(36), D(36)

C     READ A CONTROL DIGIT I
817   FORMAT (//20H MATRIX PROGRAM MM1A)
816   FORMAT (I5)
      WRITE (2,150)
818   FORMAT (/5F14.5)
1     FORMAT (100E0)
```

```
801     FORMAT (100I0)
        WRITE (2,817)
3       READ (1,801) I0
        WRITE (2,816) I0
        I1 = I0 + 3
        IF (I0 – 13) 0,0,82
        GO TO (8,9,10,11,12,13,14,15,16,17,18,19,20,21,22,23) I1
82      I1 = I0 – 13
        IF (I1 – 7) 0,0,26
        GO TO (24,25,126,127,128,129,130) I1

C       ERROR EXIT AT 26
79      FORMAT ( / 21H FAULTY CONTROL DIGIT,I5)
26      WRITE (2,79) I0

C       READ AND IGNORE UP TO NEXT –1
27      READ (1,1) A1
        IF (A1 + 1.0) 27,9,27

C       IF CODE DIGIT IS –2, PAUSE
80      FORMAT ( / 12H END OF DATA)
8       WRITE (2,150)
        WRITE (2,80)
        WRITE (2,150)
        PAUSE 8
        GO TO 3

C       CODE DIGIT –1, CLEAR MATRIX SEQUENCES TO ZEROS
9       DO 2 I = 1,1296
        A(I) = 0
2       B(I) = 0
        GO TO 3

C       CODE DIGIT 0, READ MATRIX IN ROWS AND ADD TO SEQ.
10      B1 = 1.0
701     FORMAT (E0 ,2I0)
5       READ (1,701) D1,M,N
        WRITE (2,818) D1
        DO 4 I = 1,M
        READ (1,1) (B(J), J = 1,N)
        DO 4 J = 1,N
4       A(I*N + J – N) = A(I*N + J – N) + B(J)*B1
        GO TO 3

C       CODE DIGIT 1, READ MATRIX IN ROWS AND SUBTRACT FROM SEQ.
11      B1 = –1.0
        GO TO 5
```

```
C        CODE DIGIT 2 PRE-MULTIPLY A BY INPUT MATRIX
12       READ (1,701) D1,M1,N1
         WRITE (2,818) D1
         IF (N1 – M) 26,0,26
         M2 = M1*N
         DO 6 I = 1,M2
6        B(I) = 0
         DO 28 I = 1,M1
7        READ (1,1) (C(K), K = 1,M)
         DO 28 J = 1,N
         DO 28 K = 1,M
28       B (N*I + J – N) = B(N*I + J – N) + A(N*K + J – N)*C(K)
         M = M1
         DO 90 I = 1,M
         DO 90 J = 1,N
90       A(N*I + J – N) = B(N*I + J – N)
         GO TO 3

C        CODE DIGIT 3 POST-MULTIPLY A BY INPUT MATRIX
13       READ (1,701) D1,M1,N1
         WRITE (2,818) D1
         IF (M1 – N) 26,0,26
         M3 = M*N1
         DO 30 I = 1,M3
30       B(I) = 0
         DO 31 K = 1,N
32       READ (1,1) (C(I),  I = 1,N1)
         DO 31 I = 1,M
         DO 31 J = 1,N1
31       B(N1*I + J – N1) = B(N1*I + J – N1) + A(N*I + K – N)*C(J)
         N = N1
         DO 91 I = 1,M
         DO 91 J = 1,N
91       A(N*I + J – N) = B(N*I + J – N)
         GO TO 3

C        CODE DIGIT 4 INVERT MATRIX
14       M1 = M*N
         IF (M1 – 1) 0,151,0

C        SET UP UNIT MATRIX
         DO 33 I = 1,M1
33       B(I) = 0
         N1 = N + 1
         DO 34 I = 1,M1,N1
34       B(I) =  1·0

C        CHECK THAT MATRIX IS SQUARE
```

```
          IF (M − N) 0,35,0
36        FORMAT (/18H MATRIX NOT SQUARE, F14·5)
86        WRITE (2,36) D1
          GO TO 3


C         SEEK LARGEST ELEMENT
35        DO 40 J = 1,N
          I = J
          X = 0
          DO 37 K = J,N
          Z = ABS(A(K*N + J − N))
          IF (X − Z) 0,37,37
          X = Z
          I = K
37        CONTINUE
          IF (I − J) 0,38,0


C         INTERCHANGE I AND J ROWS
          DO 41 L = 1,N
          Z = A(N*J + L − N)
          A(N*J + L − N) = A(N*I + L − N)
          A(N*I + L − N) = Z
          Y = B(N*J + L − N)
          B(N*J + L − N) = B(N*I + L − N)
41        B(N*I + L − N) = Y
38        CONTINUE


C         CHECK FOR SMALL PIVOT
          IF (ABS(A(N*J + J − N)) − 1E − 8) 0,0,39
42        FORMAT (/10H ZERO PIVOT, F14·5)
152       WRITE (2,42) D1
          GO TO 3


C         MAIN TRANSFORMATION OF BOTH MATRICES
39        J1 = J + 1
          A1 = 1·0/A(N*J + J − N)
          DO 43 L = J1,N
43        A(N*J + L − N) = A(N*J + L − N)*A1
          DO 44 L = 1,N
44        B(N*J + L − N) = B(N*J + L − N)*A1
          A(N*J + J − N) = 1·0
          DO 40 K = J1,N
          DO 46 L = J1,N
46        A(N*K + L − N) = A(N*K + L − N) − A(N*K + J − N)*A(N*J + L − N)
          DO 47 L = 1,N
47        B(N*K + L − N) = B(N*K + L − N) − A(N*K + J − N)*B(N*J + L − N)
40        A(N*K + J − N) = 0
```

```
C       BACK SUBSTITUTION
        DO 45 L = 2,N
        L1 = N − L + 2
        DO 45 K = 2,L1
        K1 = L1 − K + 1
        DO 45 J = 1,N
45      B(N*K1 + J − N) = B(N*K1 + J − N) − A(N*K1 + L1 − N)*B(N*L1 + J − N)

C       COPY INVERSE INTO A SEQ
        DO 92 I = 1,M
        DO 92 J = 1,N
92      A(N*I + J − N) = B(N*I + J − N)

C       SPECIAL CASE IF N = 1
151     IF (A(1)) 0,152,0
        B(1) = 1·0/A(1)
        A(1) = B(1)
        GO TO 3

C       DIGIT 5 PRE-MULTIPLY MATRIX BY A VECTOR
15      READ (1,701) D1,M1
        WRITE (2,818) D1
        IF (M1 − M) 0,49,0
81      FORMAT ( / 14H FAULTY VECTOR, F14·5)
50      WRITE (2,81) D1
        GO TO 27
49      CONTINUE
        READ (1,1) (D(I),  I = 1,M)
        DO 52 I = 1,N
52      C(I) = 0
        DO 53 I = 1,M
        DO 53 J = 1,N
53      C(J) = C(J) + A(N*I + J − N)*D(I)
        IP = N
        GO TO 3

C       DIGIT 6 POST-MULTIPLY MATRIX BY A VECTOR
16      READ (1,701) D1,N1
        WRITE (2,818) D1
        IF (N1 − N) 50,0,50
        DO 54 I = 1,M
54      C(I) = 0
55      READ (1,1) (D(I),  I = 1,N)
        DO 56 I = 1,M
        DO 56 J = 1,N
56      C(I) = C(I) + A(N*I + J − N)*D(J)
        IP = M
        GO TO 3
```

```
C         DIGIT 7 PRE-MULTIPLY MATRIX BY DIAGONAL MATRIX
17        READ (1,701) D1,M1
          WRITE (2,818) D1
          IF (M – M1) 50,0,50
          IF (N – M1) 50,0,50
57        READ (1,1) (C(I),  I = 1,M)
          DO 58 I = 1,M
          DO 58 J = 1,N
58        A(N*I + J – N) = A(N*I + J – N)*C(I)
          GO TO 3

C         DIGIT 8 POST-MULTIPLY MATRIX BY DIAGONAL MATRIX
18        READ (1,701) D1,N1
          WRITE (2,818) D1
          IF (M – N1) 50,0,50
          IF (N – N1) 50,0,50
59        READ (1,1) (C(I),  I = 1,N)
          DO 60 I = 1,M
          DO 60 J = 1,N
60        A(N*I + J – N) = A(N*I + J – N)*C(J)
          GO TO 3

C         DIGIT 9 PRINT A MATRIX
19        WRITE (2,150)
718       FORMAT ( / F13·4,2I4)
          WRITE (2,718) D1,M,N
819       FORMAT ( / )
          DO 61 I = 1,M
          WRITE (2,819)
          WRITE (2,818) (A(N*I + J – N),  J = 1,N)
61        CONTINUE
          WRITE (2,150)
          GO TO 3

C         DIGIT 10 PRINT C VECTOR
20        WRITE (2,150)
          WRITE (2,718) D1,IP
62        WRITE (2,818) (C(I),  I = 1,IP)
          WRITE (2,150)
          GO TO 3

C         DIGIT 11 READ VECTOR AND MULTIPLY VECTOR BY IT
21        READ (1,701) D1,N1
          WRITE (2,818) D1
          READ (1,1) (D(I),  I = 1,N1)
          X0 = 0
          DO 63 I = 1,N1
63        X0 = C(I)*D(I) + X0
```

```
          C(1) = X0
          IP = 1
          GO TO 3


C         DIGIT 12 READ A CONSTANT AND MULTIPLY THE MATRIX BY IT
22        READ (1,1) X
          WRITE (2,818) X
          DO 64 I = 1,M
          DO 64 J = 1,N
64        A(N*I + J − N) = A(N*I + J − N)*X
          GO TO 3


C         DIGIT 13 READ A CONSTANT AND MULTIPLY THE VECTOR BY IT
23        READ (1,1) X
          WRITE (2,818) X
          DO 65 I = 1,IP
65        C(I) = C(I)*X
          GO TO 3


C         DIGIT 14 TRANSPOSE A MATRIX
24        DO 66 I = 1,M
          DO 66 J = 1,N
66        B(M*J + I − M) = A(N*I + J − N)
          I = M
          M = N
          N = I
          IP = N
          DO 95 I = 1,M
          DO 95 J = 1,N
95        A(I*N + J − N) = B(I*N + J − N)
          GO TO 3


C         DIGIT 15 ADD UNIT MATRIX TO A SEQ
25        DO 71 I = 1,M
71        A(N*I + I − N) = A(N*I + I − N) + 1·0
          GO TO 3


C         DIGIT 16 DIVIDE BY SUMS ALONG ROWS OF MATRIX
126       DO 67 I = 1,M
          D(I) = 0
          DO 67 J = 1,N
67        D(I) = D(I) + A(N*I + J − N)
          IP = M
          DO 68 I = 1,M
          IF (D(I)) 69,0,69
70        FORMAT (/13H ZERO ROW SUM,I5)
          WRITE (2,70) I
          D(I) = 1E − 9
```

```
69      DO 68 J = 1,N
        C(I) = D(I)
68      A(N*I+J-N) = A(N*I+J-N)/D(I)
        GO TO 3


C       DIGIT 17 DIVIDE BY SUMS DOWN COLUMNS OF MATRIX
127     DO 72 J = 1,N
        D(J) = 0
        DO 72 I = 1,M
72      D(J) = D(J) + A(N*I+J-N)
        IP = N
        DO 74 I = 1,M
        DO 74 J = 1,N
        IF (D(J)) 74,0,74
75      FORMAT (/13H ZERO COL SUM, I5)
        WRITE (2,75) J
        D(J) = 1E-9
74      A(N*I+J-N) = A(N*I+J-N)/D(J)
        DO 98 J = 1,N
98      C(J) = D(J)
        GO TO 3


C       DIGIT 18 PRINT SUM OF ALL ELEMENTS IN MATRIX
128     A1 = 0
        DO 73 I = 1,M
        DO 73 J = 1,N
73      A1 = A1 + A(N*I+J-N)
        WRITE (2,76) A1
76      FORMAT (/19H SUM OF ELEMENTS IS,F14·5)
        GO TO 3


C       DIGIT 19 FORM KTH POWER OF MATRIX
129     READ (1,801) K
        WRITE (2,816) K
        DO 96 I = 1,M
        DO 96 J = 1,N
96      B(I*N+J-N) = A(I*N+J-N)
        IF (K-1) 3,3,0
        K = K-1
        IF (M-N) 86,0,86
83      DO 77 L = 1,K
        DO 77 I = 1,M
        DO 78 J = 1,N
        C(J) = 0
        DO 78 K1 = 1,N
78      C(J) = C(J) + B(I*N+K1-N)*A(K1*N+J-N)
        DO 77 J = 1,N
77      B(I*N+J-N) = C(J)
```

46

```
       DO 97 I = 1,M
       DO 97 J = 1,N
97     A(I*N + J − N) = B(I*N + J − N)
       GO TO 3


C      DIGIT 20 SPARE
130    WRITE (2,230)
230    FORMAT (/12H SPARE DIGIT)
       GO TO 3


C      RUNOUT FORMAT
150    FORMAT (/30H                                    ,)
       END


       FINISH
```

Note: If card input is required instead of tape input the peripheral statement should be changed to

$$\text{INPUT } 1 = \text{CR0}$$

and the three format statements at 1, 801 and 701 must be altered to the desired layout. For example

$$1 \quad \text{FORMAT } (/7 \text{ F10·5})$$

would require seven items of main data on one card. Each item would occupy 10 columns and the decimal point would be assumed at the midpoint of each ten-column number field.

§1.9 Simple test data for MM1A input

−1			Clear main sequence to zeros
0			Read matrix A_2 of size 4×3
2·0	4	3	
1·0	2·0	3·0	
4·0	5·0	6·0	
7·0	8·0	9·0	
10·0	11·0	12·0	
9			Print the matrix A_2
1			Subtract matrix A_3
3·0	4	3	
2·0	4·0	8·0	
2·0	4·0	8·0	
2·0	4·0	8·0	
2·0	4·0	8·0	
9			Print the matrix $A_2 - A_3$
2			Pre-multiply $A_2 - A_3$ by A_4
4·0	3	4	

1·0	2·0	3·0	4·0	
5·0	6·0	7·0	8·0	
9·0	10·0	11·0	12·0	
9				Print $B = A_4(A_2 - A_3)$
3				Post-multiply B by A_5
5·0	3	4		
2·0	4·0	8·0	2·0	
4·0	8·0	2·0	4·0	
8·0	2·0	4·0	8·0	
9				Print $B A_5$
−1				Clear to zeros
0				Read matrix A_6
6·0	4	4		
0·78048	−0·022767	−0·022929	−0·044674	
−0·086993	0·604873	−0·061615	−0·070382	
−0·025581	−0·043399	0·657673	−0·083222	
−0·103881	−0·111517	−0·14959	0·965826	
4				Invert A_6
9				Print A_6^{-1}
5				Pre-multiply A_6^{-1} by the vector a_{50}
50·0	4			
1·0	2·0	3·0	4·0	
10				Print $a_{50} A_6^{-1}$
6				Post-multiply A_6^{-1} by the vector a_{60}
60·0	4			
1·0	2·0	3·0	4·0	
10				Print $A_6^{-1} a_{60}$
7				Multiply A_6^{-1} by $\hat{a}_7$
7·0	4			
−1·0	−1·0	−1·0	−1·0	
9				Print $B = \hat{a}_7 A_6^{-1}$
8				
8·0	4			
−1·0	−1·0	−1·0	−1·0	
9				Print $C = B\hat{a}_7$
11				Multiply the vector a_{60} by a_9
9·0	4			
3·0	3·0	3·0	−3·0	
10				Print the scalar $a_{60} a_9$
12				Multiply B by 13·0
13·0				
9				Print 13·0B
13				Multiply a_9 by 14·0
14·0				
10				Print 14·0a_9
14				Transpose B
9				Print B'

48

| 15 | Add I to B' |
| 9 | Print $C = I + B'$ |

| 16 | Divide C by the sums along rows |
| 9 | Print matrix |

| 17 | Divide C by the sums down columns |
| 9 | Print matrix |

| 18 | Print sum of all the elements |
| −1 | Clear to zeros |

0   Read matrix A_2

$2 \cdot 0$ 3   3

$1 \cdot 0$ $2 \cdot 0$ $3 \cdot 0$

$4 \cdot 0$ $5 \cdot 0$ $6 \cdot 0$

$7 \cdot 0$ $8 \cdot 0$ $9 \cdot 0$

19   Form $B = A_2^2$

2

9   Print B

−1   Clear to zeros

−2   Stop

Note: It is always the latest matrix or vector to be calculated which is available in the store to be printed.

§1.10 Output of simple test data from MM1A

MATRIX PROGRAM MM1A

−1

0

$2 \cdot 00000$

9

$2 \cdot 0000$ 4   3

$1 \cdot 00000$	$2 \cdot 00000$	$3 \cdot 00000$
$4 \cdot 00000$	$5 \cdot 00000$	$6 \cdot 00000$
$7 \cdot 00000$	$8 \cdot 00000$	$9 \cdot 00000$
$10 \cdot 00000$	$11 \cdot 00000$	$12 \cdot 00000$

1

$3 \cdot 00000$

9

$3 \cdot 0000$ 4   3

$-1 \cdot 00000$	$-2 \cdot 00000$	$-5 \cdot 00000$
$2 \cdot 00000$	$1 \cdot 00000$	$-2 \cdot 00000$
$5 \cdot 00000$	$4 \cdot 00000$	$1 \cdot 00000$
$8 \cdot 00000$	$7 \cdot 00000$	$4 \cdot 00000$

2

4·00000

9

4·0000   3   3

50·00000	40·00000	10·00000
106·00000	80·00000	2·00000
162·00000	120·00000	−6·00000

3

5·00000

9

5·0000   3   4

340·00000	540·00000	520·00000	340·00000
548·00000	1068·00000	1016·00000	548·00000
756·00000	1596·00000	1512·00000	756·00000

−1

0

6·00000

4

9

6·0000   4   4

1·30040	0·06687	0·06772	0·07086
0·21669	1·70380	0·20165	0·15156
0·08746	0·14365	1·57111	0·14989
0·17843	0·22617	0·27391	1·08368

5

50·00000

10

50·0000   4

| 2·70980 | 4·81011 | 6·28000 | 5·15851 |

6

60·00000

10

60·0000   4

| 1·92070 | 4·83551 | 5·68772 | 5·78741 |

7

7·00000

9

7·0000   4   4

−1·30040	−0·06887	−0·06772	−0·07086
−0·21669	−1·70383	−0·20165	−0·15156
−0·08746	−0·14365	−1·57111	−0·14989
−0·17843	−0·22617	−0·27391	−1·08372

8

8·00000

9

8·0000   4   4

1·30040	0·06887	0·06772	0·07086
0·21669	1·70383	0·20165	0·15156
0·08746	0·14365	1·57111	0·14989
0·17843	0·22617	0·27391	1·08372

11

10

9·00000

9·0000　1

6·00000

12

13·00000

9

9·0000　4　4

16·90501	0·86927	0·88032	0·92112
2·81700	22·14918	2·62151	1·97028
1·13688	1·86745	20·42384	1·94861
2·31956	2·94020	3·56081	14·08878

13

14·00000

10

9·0000　4

−42·00000	−42·00000	−42·00000	42·00000

14

9

9·0000　4　4

16·90501	2·81700	1·13688	2·31956
0·86927	22·14918	1·86745	2·94020
0·88032	2·62151	20·42384	3·56081
0·92112	1·97028	1·94861	14·08878

15

9

9·0000　4　4

17·90501	2·81700	1·13688	2·31956
0·86927	23·14918	1·86745	2·94020
0·88032	2·62151	21·42384	3·56081
0·92112	1·97028	1·94861	15·08878

16

9

9·0000　4　4

0·74053	0·11651	0·04702	0·09594
0·03015	0·80307	0·06478	0·10200
0·03090	0·09202	0·75208	0·12500
0·04622	0·09887	0·09778	0·75713

17

9

	9·0000	4	4		
	0·87346		0·10492	0·04889	0·08882
	0·03557		0·72318	0·06737	0·09444
	0·03645		0·08287	0·78206	0·11573
	0·05452		0·08903	0·10168	0·70101

18

SUM OF ELEMENTS IS   4·00000

−1

0

2·00000

19

2

9

2·0000   3   3

30·00000	35·00000	40·00000
66·00000	81·00000	96·00000
102·00000	126·00000	150·00000

−2

END OF DATA

Further reading on matrix algebra will be found in Aitken (1956), Dwyer (1951), Frazer, Duncan and Collier (1946) and Goodwin (1961).

Further reading on electronic computing and Fortran will be found in Hartree (1949), Hollingdale (1959), Hollingdale and Toothill (1965), McCracken (1961) and McCracken and Dorn (1963).

2 REGRESSION ANALYSIS

SECTION 1

AN OUTLINE OF THE REGRESSION PROCESS

§2.1 Simple linear regressions

Let us suppose that we are given a set of M pairs of observations, that is observed measurements which can be thought of as points in a plane;

$$(X_1, Y_1), \ (X_2, Y_2), \ldots (X_i, Y_i), \ldots (X_M, Y_M).$$

For example, we may observe X the price of a commodity, and Y the quantity sold, and we find that $X = 42 \cdot 0d$ when $Y = 326$ thousand items sold. If we make 12 such observations we have as our initial set of data

$X =$	42·0	41·0	35·8	34·2	34·9	33·7	35·5	38·7
$Y =$	326	305	341	351	345	355	344	318
						39·7	39·7	40·1	40·2
						317	313	330	333 .

In general, we can say nothing about any mathematical laws underlying this set of observations. The computational process of regression analysis provides a way of finding and stating such mathematical laws reasonably accurately, together with measurements of the differences between the acutal observations and their theoretical counterparts.

It is a necessary feature of such a set of observations that for each observed or measured X, there should be one unique observed or measured Y, that is to say there must be a one-to-one correspondence between the set of Y's and the set of X's.

In the first place, let us assume that the connection between the X's and the Y's can be represented approximately by a linear law, so that we can plot the (X, Y)'s as a graph of points in a plane. Such a graph is called a scatter diagram.

If the points are such that we can draw an approximate straight line through them, then our initial assumption of an underlying linear law seems to be justified.

Any straight line can be represented by the equation

$$y = a + bx \tag{2.1.1}$$

where a is the distance cut off by this line, along the y axis Oy, from the origin O, and b is the slope or tangent of the angle made by the line and the x axis Ox, that is the ratio of PQ/QR where P is any point on the line. Obviously there is an infinite number of straight lines which can be drawn approximately through our set of points, and each line will have slightly different values for a and b from the next line.

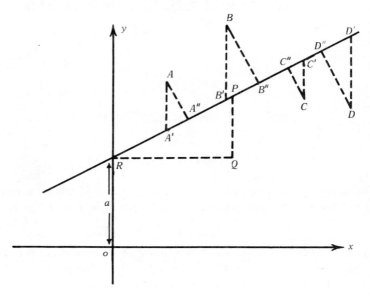

Fig. 2.1

If, however, we can make the assumption that all the errors in our observed measurements lie in the y part of each observation, and that the x's are, for our purposes, exact, then we can find values for the constants a and b in the equation (2.1.1) above, by the numerical process of 'least squares' regression analysis. We shall consider as the best regression line, or line of 'best fit', that line which has the smallest sum for the distances perpendicular to the x axis, of each observed point from the line, that is the line which gives the smallest numerical value to

$$AA' + BB' + CC' + DD'$$

in our diagram Fig. 2.1. These distances are measures of the errors between our observed values and the true underlying values. Since the numerical values of AA', BB', CC' and DD' will usually differ in sign, it is better to take the sum of the squares of these quantities

$$(AA')^2 + (BB')^2 + (CC')^2 + (DD')^2$$

as the (always positive) measure of the quantity by which all our points fail to lie exactly along a true straight line.

In our example we may be able to obtain quite good values of a and b by careful drawing and trial and error, but as yet, we have no numerical process for obtaining the true values of a and b. So now we shall assume that for each X_i and Y_i, there is a relationship of the general form

$$Y_i = a + bX_i + e_i \tag{2.1.2}$$

for $i = 1, 2, \ldots, M$, where the a and b which we wish to estimate are the same for all our observations.

The errors e_i are the deviations of the observed Y_i's from the true regression

54

line of y on x,

$$y = a + bx. \tag{2.1.3}$$

These errors e_i may be considered either as arising from the fact that our assumed linear relation does not hold exactly, or from errors of observation in the measurement of the Y_i's. It can be repeated that it is a necessary assumption of our process, that the errors arise in the Y_i's and that the X_i's are considered to be measured exactly. Thus

$$e_i = Y_i - a - bX_i \quad \text{for} \quad i = 1, 2, \ldots, M. \tag{2.1.4}$$

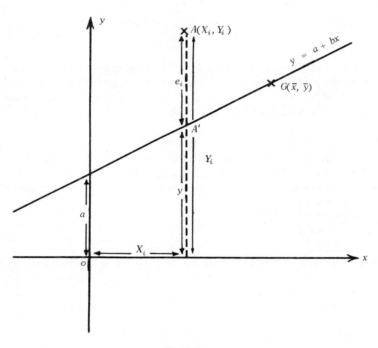

Fig. 2.2

We have assumed here that the entire error e_i in each observation arises from the observation and calculation of Y_i and not from the observation and calculation of X_i. This leads us to the regression line

$$y = a + bx$$

in which x is the independent variable and y is the dependent variable, depending on x. The quantity

$$\begin{aligned} Q &= (AA')^2 + (BB')^2 + \ldots \\ &= e_1^2 + e_2^2 + \ldots, \end{aligned} \tag{2.1.5}$$

is the sum of the squares of the distances of all the points (X_i, Y_i) from the line

$$y = a + bx$$

55

measured parallel to the Oy axis.

In this form, the regression line

$$y = a + bx$$

is best suited to provide further estimates of y from further observed or given values of x. For example, if we know that

$$y = 0 \cdot 2 + 0 \cdot 5x$$

is the line which minimizes the deviations of y measured parallel to Oy, in a certain set of data, then we can say that when $x = 0 \cdot 1$, the most likely value for y, if it belongs to the same set of data, is

$$y = 0 \cdot 2 + 0 \cdot 5 \times 0 \cdot 1$$
$$= 0 \cdot 25.$$

Equally, we could have treated Y_i as the independent variable, and X_i as the dependent variable in which all the errors arise, and then we could have minimized the sums of the squares of the e_i''s which would now be all parallel to Ox, the x axis, and this would give us a different regression line

$$y = a' + b'x. \tag{2.1.6}$$

This equation implies the assumption that all the errors arise in the observation and calculation of the X_i's, while the observed Y_i's are exact. This is the form of equation best suited to the estimation of x from a given value of y. In general the two lines

$$y = a + bx \quad \text{and} \quad y = a' + b'x$$

will not coincide.

It is a reasonable assumption that any regression line should always pass through the arithmetic mean G of any set of data. G is defined as the point

$$G(\bar{x}, \bar{y})$$

where

and
$$\left.\begin{array}{l} \bar{x} = (x_1 + x_2 + \ldots + x_N)/M, \\ \bar{y} = (y_1 + y_2 + \ldots + y_N)/M, \end{array}\right\} \tag{2.1.7}$$

and M is the total number of observations in our set of data. For example, in the set (§2.1) above

$$\bar{x} = (42 \cdot 0 + 41 \cdot 0 + \ldots + 40 \cdot 2)/12 = 445 \cdot 3/12 = 37 \cdot 1$$

and

$$\bar{y} = (326 + 305 + \ldots + 333)/12 = 3978/12 = 331 \cdot 5.$$

It is usual to shorten such expressions as

$$x_1 + x_2 + \ldots + x_M = \sum_{n=1}^{M} x_n$$

into Σx for ease of printing. In this notation

$$\bar{x} = \Sigma x/M \quad \text{and} \quad \bar{y} = \Sigma y/M. \tag{2.1.8}$$

The true regression line

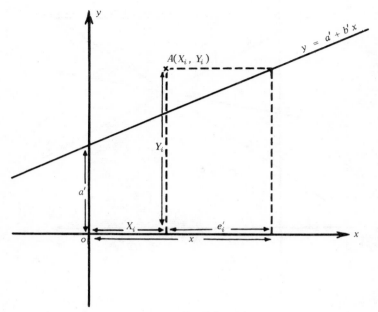

Fig. 2.3

$$y = a'' + b''x$$

can be thought of as being somewhere in the acute angle between the other two lines

$$y = a + bx \quad \text{and} \quad y = a' + b'x.$$

All three lines must pass through $G(\bar{x}, \bar{y})$ by hypothesis.

In a very favourable case, we may find that the two lines $y = a + bx$ and $y = a' + b'x$ almost coincide, so that we know the values of a'' and b'' almost exactly, in the equation $y = a'' + b''x$. But, in general, the two lines which have been drawn, through the same set of points, will only provide a guide to the upper and lower bounds of the discrepancies between the two sets of hypotheses about our errors, and they will give a very imperfect guide to the true values of a'' and b''.

The term 'regression' came into statistics from biology. The coefficient b is called the regression coefficient of y on x. It shows the percentage of y which changes for each unit change in x, that is, it shows the rate of change of y with respect to x. The coefficient a is called the constant term in the regression equation. It gives the value of y when $x = 0$. If the origin O is taken at the arithmetic mean of the data $G(\bar{x}, \bar{y})$, then the constant $a = 0$, and if the arithmetic mean of the data $G(\bar{x}, \bar{y})$, is shown by a large value of a to be a long way from the origin, then the calculation should be repeated, with the data adjusted by removal of the means, so that the new origin falls at $G(\bar{x}, \bar{y})$, in order to improve the accuracy of the calculated value for b.

We now have three conditions which the observed errors e_i have to satisfy:

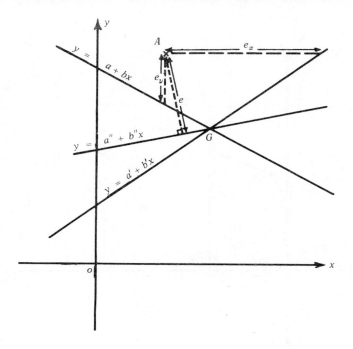

Fig. 2.4

(i) that they should not be connected with one another in any way, that is to say, that the errors arise at random, and are not due to any inbuilt bias in the data;

(ii) that the arithmetic mean of the e_i's should be zero, so that

$$(\Sigma\, e_i)/M \;=\; 0 \qquad\qquad (2.1.9)$$

This condition is a consequence of the minimizing process. The statement (2.1.9) can be re-expressed as

$$\Sigma\,(Y_i \;-\; a \;-\; b\,X_i) \;=\; 0,$$

since M is not zero, and $e_i = Y_i - a - b\,X_i$ for each value of i. The equation (2.1.9) can be re-expressed again as

$$\Sigma Y_i \;=\; M\,a \;+\; b\Sigma X_i \qquad\qquad (2.1.10)$$

since the sum of a over the M equations is Ma, and neither a nor b depend on the suffix i, so that they can be taken outside the summation symbol;

(iii) that the sum of the squares of the e_i's should be a minimum, that is that Σe_i^2 should be as small as possible. This is a simple statement of the quantity that we are trying to minimize. Now

$$\Sigma e_i^2 \;=\; \Sigma(Y_i \;-\; a \;-\; bX_i)^2,$$

and, for a minimum, we must have the change with respect to a small change in b as small as possible, or, in the notation of the calculus,

58

$$\partial(\Sigma e_i^2)/\partial b = 0,$$

which is equivalent to

$$2b\Sigma\{(Y_i - a - bX_i)X_i\} = 0. \tag{2.1.11}$$

Since we are assuming some linear connection between x and y, $b \neq 0$, so we must have

$$\Sigma X_i Y_i - a\Sigma X_i - b\Sigma X_i^2 = 0.$$

This result can be rewritten as

$$\Sigma X_i Y_i = a\Sigma X_i + b\Sigma X_i^2. \tag{2.1.12}$$

The equations (2.1.10) and (2.1.12) are called the two normal equations. They have to be solved formally to give the values for a and b which we seek. Given

$$\Sigma Y = aM + b\Sigma X$$

and

$$\Sigma XY = a\Sigma X + b\Sigma X^2,$$

let us multiply the first equation by ΣX^2 and the second equation by ΣX, so that the second terms on the right-hand sides become equal. Then our two equations become

and
$$\left.\begin{array}{l} \Sigma X^2 \Sigma Y = aM\Sigma X^2 + b\Sigma X\Sigma X^2 \\[4pt] \Sigma Y\Sigma XY = a(\Sigma X)^2 + b\Sigma X\Sigma X^2. \end{array}\right\} \tag{2.1.13}$$

If we now subtract each element of the second equation from the corresponding element of the first equation, we find that

$$\Sigma X^2 \Sigma Y - \Sigma Y\Sigma XY = aM\Sigma X^2 - a(\Sigma X)^2,$$

which gives the formula for a,

$$a = \frac{\Sigma X^2 \Sigma Y - \Sigma X\Sigma XY}{M\Sigma X^2 - (\Sigma X)^2}. \tag{2.1.14}$$

Alternatively, if we multiply the first equation by ΣX and the second equation by M, so that the first terms on the right-hand side are equal, then we have

and
$$\left.\begin{array}{l} \Sigma X\Sigma Y = aM\Sigma X + b(\Sigma X)^2 \\[4pt] M\Sigma Y = aM\Sigma X + bM\Sigma X^2. \end{array}\right\} \tag{2.1.15}$$

If we now subtract each element of the first equation from the corresponding element of the second equation, we find that

$$-\Sigma X\Sigma Y + M\Sigma XY = -b(\Sigma X)^2 + bM\Sigma X^2.$$

This gives us the formula for b,

$$b = \frac{M\Sigma XY - \Sigma X\Sigma Y}{M\Sigma X^2 - (\Sigma X)^2}. \tag{2.1.16}$$

The summation in all these sums is always from $i = 1$ to $i = M$, when there are M observations in our set of data.

When we are given our initial data, we should first examine it to see that the hypotheses about the errors are satisfied, that is:

(i) that all the errors arise at random, independently of one another, and

(ii) that they all arise in the observation of the y's rather than in the observation of the x's, since we are trying to calculate the coefficients for the regression line

$$y \;=\; a + bx.$$

The calculation to be carried out is simply the formation of the sums

$$\Sigma Y, \;\; \Sigma XY, \;\; \Sigma X, \;\; \text{and} \;\; \Sigma X^2,$$

and the substitution of their numerical values into the equations (2.1.14) and (2.1.16). These quantities are usually called the sums of squares and cross products, though they are in fact the sums of all the x items, the sum of all the y items, the sum of the squares of the x's and the sum of the cross product of each x and its own y.

The first stage is to rule out our data sheet and to enter in our headings, thus:

Title.   Date of calculation. Initials of calcula-
Source and references of data.   tor and initials of checker.

X	Y	X^2	XY
$\Sigma X =$	$\Sigma Y =$	$\Sigma X^2 =$	$\Sigma XY =$

$M \;=\;$

$$\Sigma X^2 \Sigma X \;-\; \Sigma X \Sigma XY \;=\; \qquad - \qquad =$$

$$M\Sigma X^2 \;-\; (\Sigma X)^2 \;=\; \qquad - \qquad =$$

$$M\Sigma XY \;-\; \Sigma X \Sigma Y \;=\; \qquad - \qquad =$$

$$a \;=\; \frac{\Sigma X^2 \Sigma X \;-\; \Sigma X \Sigma XY}{M\Sigma X^2 \;-\; (\Sigma X)^2} \;=\; \underline{\qquad\qquad} \;=$$

$$b \;=\; \frac{M\Sigma XY \;-\; \Sigma X \Sigma Y}{M\Sigma X^2 \;-\; (\Sigma X)^2} \;=\; \underline{\qquad\qquad} \;=$$

$$y \;=\; a + bx \;=\; \qquad + \qquad x.$$

If many such regressions are to be carried out, special computing sheets should be provided. These should be ready printed with the necessary headings, ruled columns and formulae.

Having prepared the computing sheet, we fill in the initial data in the first two columns and form the two columns of squares and products. Next we calculate the sums, and the differences of the products of the sums and enter them on our sheet. Finally we calculate the values of a and b and enter them into the equation.

12.5.61
L.J.S. C.V.

Example 1. Test data.

X	Y	X^2	XY
42·0	326	1764·00	13692·0
41·0	305	1681·00	12505·0
35·8	341	1281·64	12207·8
34·2	351	1169·64	12004·2
34·9	345	1218·01	12040·5
33·7	355	1135·69	11963·5
35·5	344	1260·25	12212·0
38·7	318	1497·69	12306·6
39·7	317	1576·09	12584·9
39·7	313	1576·09	12426·1
40·1	330	1608·01	13233·0
40·2	333	1616·04	13386·6

$$\Sigma X = 455{\cdot}5 \quad \Sigma Y = 3978 \quad \Sigma X^2 = 17384{\cdot}15 \quad \Sigma XY = 150562{\cdot}2$$

$M = 12$

$$
\begin{aligned}
\Sigma X^2 \Sigma Y - \Sigma X \Sigma XY &= 17384{\cdot}15 \times 3978 - 455{\cdot}5 \times 150562{\cdot}2, \\
&= 69154148{\cdot}7 - 68581082{\cdot}1, \\
&= 573066{\cdot}6.
\end{aligned}
$$

$$
\begin{aligned}
M\Sigma X^2 - (\Sigma X)^2 &= 12 \times 17384{\cdot}15 - (455{\cdot}5)^2, \\
&= 208609{\cdot}8 - 207480{\cdot}25, \\
&= 1129{\cdot}55.
\end{aligned}
$$

$$
\begin{aligned}
M\Sigma XY - \Sigma X \Sigma Y &= 12 \times 150562{\cdot}2 - 455{\cdot}5 \times 3978, \\
&= 1806746{\cdot}4 - 1811979{\cdot}0, \\
&= -5232{\cdot}6.
\end{aligned}
$$

$$
\begin{aligned}
a &= \frac{\Sigma X^2 \Sigma Y - \Sigma X \Sigma XY}{M\Sigma X^2 - (\Sigma X)^2} = \frac{573066{\cdot}6}{1129{\cdot}55}, \\
&= 507{\cdot}3406.
\end{aligned}
$$

$$
\begin{aligned}
b &= \frac{M\Sigma XY - \Sigma X \Sigma Y}{M\Sigma X^2 - (\Sigma X)^2} = \frac{-5232{\cdot}6}{1129{\cdot}55}, \\
&= -4{\cdot}63246.
\end{aligned}
$$

$$y = a + bx,$$
$$y = 507{\cdot}3406 - 4{\cdot}63246x.$$

When some types of electric hand calculating machines are being used, after some practice, it is not necessary to write down each item in the X^2 and the XY columns, as these totals can be accumulated in the machine and written down immediately, in their proper places on the computing sheet.

We have shown two decimal places in the above example, except in the final division. Now we might ask how many of the digits given above have any real meaning. The initial data for X and Y are pairs of numbers observed from reality, so we can assume an error of about half a unit in the last digit shown. Otherwise another digit could have been given. Thus when the data says that $X = 42 \cdot 0$ when $Y = 326$, what we are really saying is that, as near as it can be measured,

$$X = 42 \cdot 0 \pm 0 \cdot 05 \quad \text{when} \quad Y = 326 \pm 0 \cdot 5$$

If we repeat the calculation with only one item of the initial data changed, that is the first observation of X changed into $42 \cdot 1$, say, we shall find that the first figure after the decimal point is altered throughout, up to the final divisions in the calculations of a and b and that the fifth figures in both a and b are altered. As a rough guide, the final result contains the same number of trust-worthy figures as are present in ΣX and ΣY. Thus here ΣX and ΣY have four reasonably good figures in each, so that a and b will be accurate to four figures each also.

Another source of lost accuracy in this type of calculation is in the formation of the three differences

$$\Sigma X^2 \Sigma Y - \Sigma X \Sigma XY, \quad M \Sigma X^2 - (\Sigma X)^2 \quad \text{and} \quad M \Sigma XY - \Sigma X \Sigma Y.$$

It can happen for example that $\Sigma X^2 \Sigma Y$ is nearly equal to $\Sigma X \Sigma XY$, and then nearly all the significant figures present at the start of the calculation are lost. This trouble can be relieved by taking the differences in the forms

$$\Sigma X^2 \Sigma Y \{ 1 - (\Sigma X \Sigma XY)/(\Sigma X^2 \Sigma Y) \}$$
$$M \Sigma X^2 \{ 1 - (\Sigma X)^2/(M \Sigma X^2) \} \qquad \text{and}$$
$$M \Sigma XY \{ 1 - (\Sigma X \Sigma Y)/(M \Sigma XY) \}.$$

Frequently, the origin of the data is transformed into the arithmetic mean $G(\overline{X}, \overline{Y})$, where

$$\overline{X} = \Sigma X/M \quad \text{and} \quad \overline{Y} = \Sigma Y/M \qquad (2.2.1)$$

as usual. This leads, in theory, to exactly the same results in a and b. In practice, it usually produces more accurate estimates for a and b, particularly when, as in our example, the origin is a long way from G. We can see that all the x measurements are somewhere near 35 and that all the y measurements are near 330. So G is somewhere near $(35, 330)$, and our estimates will be improved by the removal of the means. The formulae for a and b are very much simpler, though our computing sheet requires two extra columns. The formulae for a and b now become

$$a = \overline{Y} - b\overline{X},$$

and
$$b = \Sigma(X - \overline{X})(Y - \overline{Y})/\Sigma(X - \overline{X})^2, \qquad (2.2.2)$$

since always
$$\Sigma(X - \overline{X}) = 0 \quad \text{and} \quad \Sigma(Y - \overline{Y}) = 0,$$
by definition.

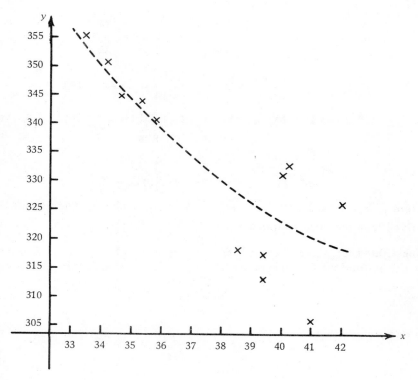

Fig. 2.5

Example 2. Test data.

12.5.61

L.J.S.   C.V.

X	Y	$X - \bar{X}$	$Y - \bar{Y}$	$(X - \bar{X})^2$	$(X - \bar{X})(Y - \bar{Y})$
42·0	326	4·04	−5·5	16·32	−22·22
41·0	305	3·04	−26·5	9·24	−80·56
35·8	341	−2·16	9·5	4·67	−20·52
34·2	351	−3·76	19·5	14·14	−73·32
34·9	345	−3·06	13·5	9·36	−41·31
33·7	355	−4·26	23·5	18·15	−100·11
35·5	344	−2·46	12·5	6·05	−30·75
38·7	318	0·74	−13·5	0·55	− 9·99
39·7	317	1·74	−14·5	3·03	−25·23
39·7	313	1·74	−18·5	3·03	−32·19
40·1	330	2·14	−1·5	4·58	−3·21
40·2	333	2·24	1·5	5·02	3·36
$\Sigma X =$ 455·5	$\Sigma Y =$ 3978	$\Sigma(X - \bar{X}) = 0$	$\Sigma(Y - \bar{Y}) = 0$	$\Sigma(X - \bar{X})^2 =$ 94·14	$\Sigma(X - \bar{X})(Y - \bar{Y}) =$ −436·05

$$M = 12,$$

$$\overline{X} = \Sigma X/M = 37 \cdot 96,$$

$$\overline{Y} = \Sigma Y/M = 331 \cdot 50,$$

$$b = \frac{\Sigma(X - \overline{X})(Y - \overline{Y})}{\Sigma(X - \overline{X})^2} = \frac{-436 \cdot 05}{94 \cdot 14} = -4 \cdot 63193,$$

$$a = \overline{Y} - b\overline{X} = 331 \cdot 50 - (-4 \cdot 63193) \times 37 \cdot 96,$$

$$= 331 \cdot 50 + 175 \cdot 828,$$

$$= 507 \cdot 328.$$

$$y = a + bx = 507 \cdot 328 - 4 \cdot 63193x.$$

Here $\Sigma(X - \overline{X})$ and $\Sigma(Y - \overline{Y})$ are calculated as a check. The formula for b is derived from the original formula $b = \dfrac{M\Sigma XY - \Sigma X \Sigma Y}{M\Sigma X^2 - (\Sigma X)^2}$, when $X - \overline{X}$ and $Y - \overline{Y}$ are substituted for X and Y, as $\Sigma(X - \overline{X}) = 0$ and $\Sigma(Y - \overline{Y}) = 0$. The formula for a comes from the fact that when the regression line goes through G, we have

$$y - \overline{Y} = b(x - \overline{X}), \qquad \text{that is}$$

$$y = (\overline{Y} - b\overline{X}) + bx.$$

From this we see that

$$a = \overline{Y} - b\overline{X}. \tag{2.2.3}$$

In general there are two big advantages to be gained from such a transformation in all regression calculations, despite the additional work involved in forming the extra columns. Firstly, the actual calculations and the formulae used are all simplified, and secondly, there is always a gain in the accuracy of the calculation of a and b. The calculation of both these items requires the formation of the difference of two quantities. If the means are not removed first, these two quantities may be almost equal to one another. But if the means are removed first, from the original data, the actual significant figures which are present in the calculation at this point, are made more apparent.

§2.3 Curvilinear regression

Other simple transformations are often applied to X and Y before the carrying out of the regression process. Thus we might take as our set of initial data, not the original (X, Y)'s but $(\log_e X, \log_e Y)$ or (e^X, e^Y) or any other simple transformation which may seem to bring the data more or less into an approximate linear form.

The usual process is to draw a graph through the initial (X, Y)'s and then to inspect the resulting line, to see if it is approximately a straight line already, when no transformation is needed, or whether it is almost an exponential curve or a logarithmic curve, or if it looks like some other simple curve.

As an example of such a transformation, let us look again at the short set of data used in the previous example, and this time, as a preliminary, let us plot the points on a graph.

It seems, from inspection, that a gentle curve might pass more closely to these points than any straight line, so we shall try to fit the curve

$$\log_e y = a + b \log_e x, \qquad (2.3.1)$$

and make the transformation in our data

$$Y = \log_e y, \quad X = \log_e x. \qquad (2.3.2)$$

Example 3.

X	Y	$X - \bar{X}$	$Y - \bar{Y}$	$(X - \bar{X})^2$	$(X - \bar{X})(Y - \bar{Y})$
3·738	5·787	0·104	−0·016	0·010816	−0·001664
3·714	5·720	0·080	−0·083	0·006400	−0·006640
3·578	5·832	−0·056	0·029	0·003136	−0·001624
3·532	5·861	−0·102	0·058	0·010404	−0·005916
3·552	5·844	−0·082	0·041	0·006724	−0·003362
3·518	5·872	−0·116	0·069	0·013456	−0·008004
3·570	5·841	−0·064	0·038	0·004096	−0·002432
3·656	5·762	0·022	−0·041	0·000484	−0·000902
3·681	5·759	0·047	−0·044	0·002209	−0·002068
3·681	5·746	0·047	−0·057	0·002209	−0·002679
3·691	5·799	0·057	−0·004	0·003249	−0·000228
3·694	5·808	0·060	0·005	0·003600	0·000300
$\Sigma X =$ 43·605	$\Sigma Y =$ 69·631			$\Sigma(X - \bar{X})^2 =$ 0·066783	$\Sigma(X - \bar{X})(Y - \bar{Y}) =$ −0·035219

$$M = 12, \quad \bar{X} = 3·634, \quad \bar{Y} = 5·803.$$

$$b = \frac{\Sigma(X - \bar{X})(Y - \bar{Y})}{\Sigma(X - \bar{X})^2} = \frac{-0·035219}{0·066783} = -0·527365.$$

$$a = \bar{Y} - b\bar{X} = 5·803 - (-1·916) = 7·719.$$

$$Y = a + bX = 7·719 - 0·5274 X.$$

§2.4 Further statistics

In order to proceed further we must look again at some of our assumptions about the behaviour of the errors e_i. Here we have a certain choice of assumptions. The assumptions we shall make are amongst the commonest and simplest, but whatever assumptions are made, they should be examined against each set of data to see if in fact they hold for that set of data.

The error e_i is defined as the difference between the actual ith observation of y, Y_i, and the calculated value of y, $a + bX_i$, that is

$$e_i = Y_i - (a + bX_i). \qquad (2.4.1)$$

The variance s^2 is defined as the arithmetic mean of the sum of the squares of the deviations of the errors e_i from this mean.

We assume now

E

(i) that the errors e_1, e_2, ..., e_i, ..., e_M, are all independent of one another;

(ii) that the errors are distributed normally with their arithmetic mean zero, and their variance s^2, so that the distribution of a single error e_i, is defined as

$$P_i = \frac{1}{\sqrt{2\pi s}} \exp\left(-\frac{1}{2s^2} e_i^2\right). \tag{2.4.2}$$

This is the probability that a single error will have a size e_i. This distribution, represented by (2.4.2), is called the normal distribution. (See Brookes and Dick (1955) Chapter 6, or any elementary book on statistics for a full discussion of the normal curve). Since the errors e_i are independent of one another, the probability that the whole set

$$(e_1, ..., e_M)$$

will occur together is given by the product

$$P_1 P_2 \ldots P_M = \left(\frac{1}{\sqrt{2\pi s}}\right)^M \exp\left\{\frac{-1}{2s^2} [e_1^2 + e_2^2 + \ldots + e_M^2]\right\}$$

$$= \left(\frac{1}{\sqrt{2\pi s}}\right)^M \exp\left(\frac{-1}{2s^2} Q\right), \tag{2.4.3}$$

where $\qquad Q = e_1^2 + \ldots + e_M^2.$

Since $\qquad e_i = Y_i - a - bX_i,$

$$Q = (Y_1 - a - bX_1)^2 + \ldots + (Y_M - a - bX_M)^2. \tag{2.4.4}$$

Q is in fact the sum of the squares of the deviations of the observed values

$$Y_1, Y_2, \ldots Y_i, \ldots Y_M$$

from the calculated values

$$a + bX_1, \ldots, a + bX_i, \ldots, a + bX_M.$$

In order to get the best possible fit of the line $y = a + bX$ to the observed data, it is necessary to find values of a and b which make Q as small as possible.

Let us then form the partial derivatives of Q with respect to a and b.

We find that $\qquad \dfrac{\partial Q}{\partial a} = -2\Sigma(Y_i - a - bX_i),$

and $\qquad \dfrac{\partial Q}{\partial b} = -2\Sigma X_i (Y_i - a - bX_i).$ $\qquad$ (2.4.5)

For Q to be a minimum these quantities must be zero,

that is $\qquad \Sigma(Y_i - a - bX_i) = 0,$

and $\qquad \Sigma X_i (Y_i - a - bX_i) = 0.$ $\qquad$ (2.4.6)

These equations can be rewritten

$$\Sigma Y_i = Ma + b\Sigma X_i,$$

and $\qquad \Sigma X_i Y_i = a\Sigma X_i + b\Sigma X_i^2.$ $\qquad$ (2.4.7)

These are again the two normal equations.

In order to be able to form some opinions as to the accuracy and closeness of fit of our regression line

$$y = a + bx$$

when we have obtained values for a and b, we can calculate the following statistics:

$$s^2 = \frac{\Sigma Y^2 - a\Sigma Y - b\Sigma XY}{M - 2}, \tag{2.4.8}$$

$$R_1^2 = \frac{(a\Sigma Y + b\Sigma XY)}{\Sigma Y^2}, \tag{2.4.9}$$

$$R_2^2 = \frac{(\Sigma Y)^2/M - a\Sigma Y - b\Sigma XY}{(\Sigma Y)^2/M - \Sigma Y^2}, \tag{2.4.10}$$

$$se\,(a) = \sqrt{[s^2(\Sigma X^2/M)/\{\Sigma X^2 - (\Sigma X)^2/M\,\}]}, \tag{2.4.11}$$

$$t_a = a/se(a), \tag{2.4.12}$$

$$se\,(b) = \sqrt{[s^2/\{\Sigma X^2 - (\Sigma X)^2/M\,\}]}, \tag{2.4.13}$$

and

$$t_b = b/se(b). \tag{2.4.14}$$

Here s^2 is called the estimated variance. It is the estimate of s^2, calculated from the estimated a and b.

R_1^2 and R_2^2 are correlation coefficients. They measure the goodness of fit of the whole line $y = a + bx$ in two different ways. $se(b)$ is the standard error of b. It measures the error in the calculation of b and t_b is the t-ratio. The t-ratio is used in tests of significance, of the difference between the estimated and hypothetical regression coefficient, that is the ratio of the estimated value b to its standard error.

Sometimes also we are required to calculate the values of the calculated y_i's, without errors and the values of the residuals e_i. Since

$$y = a + bx \quad \text{and} \quad x = X_i \quad \text{when} \quad y = Y_i, \quad \text{exactly,}$$

we have

$$y_i = a + bX_i \quad \text{for} \quad i = 1, 2, \ldots M, \quad \text{and}$$

$$e_i = Y_i - y_i. \tag{2.4.15}$$

Here e_i is the difference between Y_i, the original observed value of y, and y_i the value of y calculated from the observed values of X_i. These values are usually entered up in two further columns on our computing sheet.

Another useful statistic which is often required is the Durban-Watson d-statistic. This is defined as

$$d = \frac{\sum_{i=2}^{M} (e_i - e_{i-1})^2}{\sum_{i=1}^{M} e_i^2}. \tag{2.4.16}$$

In examples 2 and 3, we have fitted two different regression lines to the same set of data and we may ask the question:— which of the two lines gives the better result? To decide this, we have to look more closely at the four statistics s^2,

R_1^2, R_2^2 and d.

The quantity $a + b\Sigma XY$ is the measure of the sums of the quadrilaterals $X_i Y_i$ formed by the coordinates of the observed points (X_i, Y_i), each multiplied by the calculated quantity b. The quantity ΣY^2 is the sum of the squares of the observed distances Y_i of each point (X_i, Y_i) from the Y axis. The best fit is the line which makes as small as possible the sum of the deviations of the calculated points from the observed points, but this deviation for one point is $Y_i - a - bX_i$.

So if we multiply by Y_i and add over all the points $\Sigma(Y_i^2 - aY_i - bX_i Y_i) = \Sigma Y^2 - a\Sigma Y - b\Sigma XY$ is a measure of this sum. In particular, the line (2.3.1) with the smaller $s^2 = (\Sigma Y^2 - a\Sigma Y - b\Sigma XY)/(M-2)$ is the better of the two regression lines.

The ratio

$$R_1^2 = (a\Sigma Y + b\Sigma XY)/\Sigma Y^2 \qquad (2.4.17)$$

is the ratio of the calculated to the observed deviations and it should be somewhat smaller than unity, since we assume that some, but not all of the observed error in the Y_i is explained by fitting $a + bX_i$ in place of Y_i.

The ratio

$$R_2^2 = 1 - \frac{\Sigma Y^2 - a\Sigma Y - b\Sigma XY}{\Sigma Y^2 - (\Sigma Y)^2/M} \qquad (2.4.18)$$

is the measure of the same ratio as R_1^2 but this time the observations are taken as deviations from the mean $G(\overline{X}, \overline{Y})$, instead of being based on an arbitrary origin O. For this reason R_2^2 gives a more accurate measure of the ratio than R_1^2. If however the means have been removed from the initial data before carrying out the regression calculation then $R_1^2 = R_2^2$.

The Durbin-Watson statistic

$$d = \sum_{i=2}^{M}(e_i - e_{i-1})^2 \Big/ \sum_{i=1}^{M} e_i^2 \qquad (2.4.19)$$

forms a more sophisticated test of the behaviour of the errors e_i. Now

$$e_i = Y_i - a - bX_i, \qquad (2.4.20)$$

and

$$\Delta e_i = e_i - e_{i-1} = (Y_i - Y_{i-1}) - b(X_i - X_{i-1}). \qquad (2.4.21)$$

So Σe_i^2 is the sum of the squares of the differences between the observed Y_i's and their calculated values $a + bX_i$. Also $\Sigma\Delta e_i^2$ is the sum of the squares of these differences between one observation and its neighbours. The ratio d provides a measure of any auto-correlation or lack of random behaviour in the calculated residuals e_i, which are, of course, first approximations to the values of the true errors ϵ_i. This statistic will warn us immediately if any of the necessary hypotheses about the behaviour of the e_i's are unwittingly violated.

Our ready-prepared computing sheet should have space for these extra columns and statistics, so that our complete calculating sheet looks like this.

Example 4.

X_i	Y_i	$y_i = a + bX_i$	$e_i = Y_i - y_i$	$\Delta e_i = e_i - e_{i-1}$
42·0	326	313	13	
41·0	305	317	−12	−25
35·8	341	341	0	12
34·2	351	349	2	2
34·9	345	346	− 1	− 3
33·7	355	351	4	5
35·5	344	343	1	− 3
38·7	318	328	− 10	− 11
39·7	317	323	− 6	4
39·7	313	323	− 10	− 4
40·1	330	322	8	18
40·2	333	321	12	4
$\Sigma X = $ 455·5	$\Sigma Y = $ 3978	$\Sigma y_i = $ 3977	$\Sigma e_i = 1$	$\Sigma \Delta e_i = 1$

$M = 12$, $\Sigma X^2 = 17384 \cdot 15$, $\Sigma XY = 150562 \cdot 2$, $\Sigma Y^2 = 1{,}321{,}540$.

$$a = \frac{\Sigma X^2 \Sigma Y - \Sigma X \Sigma XY}{M \Sigma X^2 - (\Sigma X)^2} = \frac{573066 \cdot 6}{1129 \cdot 55} = 507 \cdot 341.$$

$$b = \frac{M \Sigma XY - \Sigma X \Sigma Y}{M \Sigma X^2 - (\Sigma X)^2} = \frac{-5232 \cdot 6}{1129 \cdot 55} = -4 \cdot 6325.$$

$$y = a + bx = 507 \cdot 341 - 4 \cdot 6325 x.$$

$a \Sigma Y + b \Sigma XY = 507 \cdot 341 \times 3978 - 4 \cdot 6325 \times 150562 \cdot 2 = 1320723 \cdot 1065.$

$$s^2 = \frac{\Sigma Y^2 - a \Sigma Y - b \Sigma XY}{M - 2},$$

$$= 81 \cdot 689.$$

$$R_1^2 = \frac{a \Sigma Y + b \Sigma XY}{\Sigma Y^2} = \frac{1{,}320{,}723 \cdot 1065}{1{,}321{,}540} = 0 \cdot 99938186.$$

$$R_2^2 = 1 - \frac{\Sigma Y^2 - (a \Sigma Y + b \Sigma XY)}{\Sigma Y^2 - (\Sigma Y)^2/M} = 1 - \frac{1{,}321{,}540 - 1{,}320{,}723 \cdot 1065}{1{,}321{,}540 - (3978)^2/12},$$

$$= 1 - \frac{816 \cdot 8935}{2833} = 1 - 0 \cdot 2883 = 0 \cdot 7117.$$

$\text{se}(b) = \sqrt{[s^2/\{\Sigma X^2 - (\Sigma X)^2/M\}]} = \sqrt{(0 \cdot 86783)} = 0 \cdot 9316.$

$t_b = b/\text{se}(b) = -4 \cdot 6325/0 \cdot 9316 = -4 \cdot 973,$

$\Sigma e_i^2 = 779,$

$\Sigma \Delta e_i^2 = 1309,$

and
$$d = \Sigma \Delta e_i^2 / \Sigma e_i^2 = 1309/779 = 1\cdot6804.$$

It is a useful check to note that, $\dfrac{\Sigma e_i^2}{M-2} \simeq s^2$ provided that the calculations have been done correctly. Here

$$\frac{\Sigma e_i^2}{M-2} = 77\cdot9 \simeq s^2 \qquad (2.4.22)$$

If we transform the initial data to have its origin at the arithmetic mean, our new statistics become

$$s^2 = \frac{\Sigma(Y-\overline{Y})^2 - b\Sigma(X-\overline{X})(Y-\overline{Y})}{M-2}, \qquad (2.4.23)$$

$$R_1^2 = \frac{b\Sigma(X-\overline{X})(Y-\overline{Y})}{\Sigma(Y-\overline{Y})^2} = R_2^2, \qquad (2.4.24)$$

$$se(b) = \sqrt{[s^2/\Sigma(X-\overline{X})^2]}, \qquad (2.4.25)$$

and
$$t_b = b/se(b). \qquad (2.4.26)$$

Our example now looks like this:

Example 5.

X_i	Y_i	$X_i - \overline{X}$	$Y_i - \overline{Y}$	$\begin{aligned} y_i - \overline{y} = \\ b(X_i - \overline{X}) \end{aligned}$	$\begin{aligned} e_i = \\ (Y_i - \overline{Y}) \\ -(y_i - \overline{y}) \end{aligned}$	$\begin{aligned} \Delta e_i = \\ e_i - e_{i-1} \end{aligned}$
42·0	326	+4·04	−5·5	−18·72	+13·22	
41·0	305	+3·04	−26·5	−14·08	−12·42	−25·64
35·8	341	−2·16	+9·5	+10·01	−0·51	+11·91
34·2	351	−3·76	+19·5	+17·42	+2·08	+2·59
34·9	345	−3·06	+13·5	+14·18	−0·68	−2·76
33·7	355	−4·26	+23·5	+19·73	+3·77	+4·45
35·5	344	−2·46	+12·5	+11·40	+1·10	−2·67
38·7	318	+0·74	−13·5	−3·43	−10·07	−11·17
39·7	317	+1·74	−14·5	−8·06	−6·44	+3·63
39·7	313	+1·74	−18·5	−8·06	−10·44	+4·00
40·1	330	+2·14	−1·5	−9·91	+8·41	+18·85
40·2	333	+2·24	+1·5	−10·38	+11·88	+3·47

$\Sigma X =$ $\Sigma Y =$
455·5   3978

$$M = 12, \quad \overline{X} = 37\cdot96, \quad \overline{Y} = 331\cdot50.$$

$$\Sigma(X-\overline{X})^2 = 94\cdot129, \quad \Sigma(X-\overline{X})(Y-\overline{Y}) = -436\cdot05, \quad \Sigma(Y-\overline{Y})^2 = 2833\cdot0.$$

$$b = \frac{\Sigma(X-\overline{X})(Y-\overline{Y})}{\Sigma(X-\overline{X})^2} = -4\cdot63247.$$

$$a = \overline{Y} - b\overline{X} = 507\cdot349.$$

$$y = a + bx = 507\cdot349 - 4\cdot632x.$$

$$s^2 = \frac{\Sigma(Y - \overline{Y})^2 - b\Sigma(X - \overline{X})(Y - \overline{Y})}{M - 2} = 81\cdot3011.$$

$$R_1^2 = \frac{b\Sigma(X - \overline{X})(Y - \overline{Y})}{\Sigma(Y - \overline{Y})^2} = R_2^2 = \frac{2019\cdot9885}{2833\cdot0} = 0\cdot71302.$$

$$se(b) = \sqrt{[s^2/\Sigma(X - \overline{X})^2]} = \sqrt{(0\cdot863720)} = 0\cdot9294.$$

$$t_b = b/se(b) = -4\cdot984.$$

$$\Sigma e_i^2 = 813\cdot2312,$$

$$\Sigma \Delta e_i^2 = 1361\cdot8240,$$

and $\quad d = \Sigma \Delta e_i^2 / \Sigma e_i^2 = 1\cdot6746.$

Check $\quad \dfrac{\Sigma e_i^2}{M - 2} \simeq s^2,$ that is $813\cdot2312/10 \simeq 81\cdot3011.$

Here d should be unchanged in value, since

$$e_i = (Y_i - \overline{Y}) - (y_i - \overline{y}) \simeq Y_i - y_i \qquad (2.4.27)$$

as before.

§2.5 Weighted regression

Frequently we may feel that a greater importance should be attached to one observation rather than to another. For example, suppose that our test data had been made as prices and quantities sold of some commodities over a period of 120 days, and that our first price $X = 4$, for the quantity $Y = 7\cdot75$ had occurred on twenty days, the second price on 40 days, the third on 50 days and the last price on only 10 days.

Obviously it would be wrong to treat our four prices on an equal basis as we did above, and it is more sensible to attach weights to each price and quantity, so that our initial data matrix is

w	X	Y
20	4	7·75
40	9	7·92
50	14	8·17
10	19	8·25

The complete calculation looks like this, when we do not remove the means:

71

Example 6

W_i	X_i	Y_i	wX_i	wY_i	y_i $= a + bX_i$	$e_i =$ $Y_i - y_i$	$\Delta e_i =$ $e_i - e_{i-1}$
20	4	7·75	80	155	7·75	0·002	−0·024
40	9	7·92	360	316·8	7·94	−0·022	−0·024
50	14	8·17	700	408·5	8·13	0·033	0·055
10	19	8·25	190	82·5	8·33	−0·081	−0·114

$$M = 4, \quad \Sigma w = 120, \quad \Sigma wX = 1330, \quad \Sigma wY = 962\cdot 8,$$

$$\Sigma wX^2 = 16970, \quad \Sigma wXY = 10757\cdot 7, \quad \Sigma wY^2 = 7728\cdot 38,$$

$$a = \frac{\Sigma wX^2 \Sigma wY - \Sigma wX \Sigma wXY}{\Sigma w \Sigma wX^2 - (\Sigma wX)^2} = 7\cdot 592,$$

$$b = \frac{\Sigma w \Sigma wXY - \Sigma wX \Sigma wY}{\Sigma w \Sigma wX^2 - (\Sigma wX)^2} = 0\cdot 0389,$$

$$y = a + bx = 7\cdot 59 + 0\cdot 0389x.$$

§2.6 Multiple regressions

The simple linear regression of one dependent variable y, on one independent variable x, in principle, can be extended easily to a multiple regression of one dependent variable y on a whole set of independent variables $x_1, x_2, ..., x_N$. Each observation involves $N + 1$ measurements and the whole set of M observations has the form $(Y_i, X_{i1}, X_{i2}, ..., X_{ij}, ..., X_{iN})$ where $i = 1, 2, ..., i, ..., M$, and $j = 1, 2, ..., j, ..., N$.

Before we go on to the general case, we will consider first the case when $N = 2$ which can be done easily using hand-machines, by simple extensions of the previous calculations for $N = 1$. An electronic computer should be used if N is at all large, say $N > 5$. It is rare to find any attempt made at regression for $N > 20$, as then the practical difficulties of assigning meanings to the various X's become insoluble.

When $N = 2$, we have one column of Y_i's and two columns of X's, X_{i1} and X_{i2}, in our initial data. Again these may have arisen as the result of direct observation, or as the result of simple transformations, such as $\log_e X$ or e^X, of our original data. We assume that all the error in each case is concentrated in the Y of the observation, so that

$$Y_i = a + b_1 X_{i1} + b_2 X_{i2} + e_i, \quad i = 1, 2, ..., M. \tag{2.6.1}$$

Again we assume that $e_1, ..., e_M$ all arise independently of one another and that they are distributed normally with zero arithmetic mean, and variance s^2. As in the case $N = 1$,

$$P_i = \left(\frac{1}{\sqrt{2\pi}s}\right) \exp\left(-\frac{1}{2s^2} e_i^2\right), \tag{2.6.2}$$

and
$$P_1 P_2 \ldots P_M = \left(\frac{1}{\sqrt{2\pi}s}\right)^M \exp\left(-\frac{1}{2s^2}Q\right), \tag{2.6.3}$$

where
$$Q = \Sigma e_i^2 = \sum_{i=1}^{M} (Y_i - a - b_1 X_{i_1} - b_2 X_{i_2})^2 \tag{2.6.4}$$

We require to find values of a, b_1, and b_2 which minimize Q. Now, if we drop the suffix i, over which the summation is carried out, we have

$$\left.\begin{aligned}
\frac{\partial Q}{\partial a} &= -2\Sigma(Y - a - b_1 X_1 - b_2 X_2) \\[2mm]
\frac{\partial Q}{\partial b_1} &= -2\Sigma X_1 (Y - a - b_1 X_1 - b_2 X_2) \\[2mm]
\frac{\partial Q}{\partial b_2} &= -2\Sigma X_2 (Y - a - b_1 X_1 - b_2 X_2),
\end{aligned}\right\} \tag{2.6.5}$$

and for a minimum we must have

$$\frac{\partial Q}{\partial a} = \frac{\partial Q}{\partial b_1} = \frac{\partial Q}{\partial b_2} = 0. \tag{2.6.6}$$

Hence our normal equations are now

$$\left.\begin{aligned}
\Sigma Y - aM - b_1 \Sigma X_1 - b_2 \Sigma X_2 &= 0 \\
\Sigma X_1 Y - a\Sigma X_1 - b_1 \Sigma X_1^2 - b_2 \Sigma X_1 X_2 &= 0 \\
\Sigma X_2 Y - a\Sigma X_2 - b_1 \Sigma X_1 X_2 - b_2 \Sigma X_2^2 &= 0.
\end{aligned}\right\} \tag{2.6.7}$$

These equations are now a set of simultaneous equations in a, b_1, and b_2, and we have to solve them, to obtain numerical values of a, b_1 and b_2. Our final regression equation is then

$$y = a + b_1 x_1 + b_2 x_2. \tag{2.6.8}$$

The main difficulty in such a calculation lies in solving the normal equations. The explicit algebraic formulae for a, b_1 and b_2, for $N = 2$, when means are not removed, are rather complicated and will not be given here. It is now even more vital in hand-calculation that the arithmetic means $\overline{X}_i$ and $\overline{Y}$ be removed first, from our calculations. When this is done the normal equations become

$$\left.\begin{aligned}
\Sigma(X_1 - \overline{X}_1)(Y - \overline{Y}) - b_1 \Sigma(X_1 - \overline{X}_1)^2 - b_2 \Sigma(X_1 - \overline{X}_1)(X_2 - \overline{X}_2) &= 0 \\
\Sigma(X_2 - \overline{X}_2)(Y - \overline{Y}) - b_1 \Sigma(X_1 - \overline{X}_1)(X_2 - \overline{X}_2) - b_2 \Sigma(X_2 - \overline{X}_2)^2 &= 0,
\end{aligned}\right\} \tag{2.6.9}$$

and

since now
$$\Sigma(Y - \overline{Y}) = \Sigma(X_1 - \overline{X}_1) = \Sigma(X_2 - \overline{X}_2) = 0.$$

The explicit formulae for b_1 and b_2 are

$$b_1 = \frac{\Sigma(X_2 - \overline{X}_2)(Y - \overline{Y})\,\Sigma(X_1 - \overline{X}_1)(X_2 - \overline{X}_2) - \Sigma(X_1 - \overline{X}_1)(Y - \overline{Y})\,\Sigma(X_2 - \overline{X}_2)^2}{\{\Sigma(X_1 - \overline{X}_1)(X_2 - \overline{X}_2)\}^2 - \Sigma(X_1 - \overline{X}_1)^2\,\Sigma(X_2 - \overline{X}_2)^2}$$

and

$$b_2 = \frac{\Sigma(X_1 - \overline{X}_1)(Y - \overline{Y})\,\Sigma(X_2 - \overline{X}_2)(X_1 - \overline{X}_1) - \Sigma(X_2 - \overline{X}_2)(Y - \overline{Y})\,\Sigma(X_1 - \overline{X}_1)^2}{\{\Sigma(X_2 - \overline{X}_2)(X_1 - \overline{X}_1)\}^2 - \Sigma(X_2 - \overline{X}_2)^2\,\Sigma(X_1 - \overline{X}_1)^2}$$

$$\tag{2.6.10}$$

It should be noted that these formulae are symmetric in X_1 and X_2. The regression equation is now

$$y - \overline{Y} = b_1(x_1 - \overline{X}_1) + b_2(x_2 - \overline{X}_2),$$

that is

$$y = (\overline{Y} - b_1\overline{X}_1 - b_2\overline{X}_2) + b_1 x_1 + b_2 x_2. \qquad (2.6.11)$$

§2.7 Layout of multiple regressions in two variables

The layout of the computing sheet for hand calculations is similar to the simpler case with one variable, but there are two extra columns for the extra variable.

Example 7

Y	X_1	X_2	$Y - \overline{Y}$	$X_1 - \overline{X}_1$	$X_2 - \overline{X}_2$	y	$e = Y-y$	$\Delta e = e_i - e_{i-1}$
78·5	7	60	−16·9	−0·5	30	76·3	2·2	
74·3	1	52	−21·1	−6·5	22	72·6	1·7	−0·5
104·3	11	20	8·9	3·5	−10	104·3	0	−1·7
87·6	11	47	−7·8	3·5	17	90·1	−2·5	−2·5
95·9	7	33	0·5	−0·5	3	92·9	3·0	5·5
109·2	11	22	13·8	3·5	−8	106·4	2·8	−0·2
102·7	3	6	7·3	−4·5	−24	103·7	−1·0	−3·8
72·5	1	44	−22·9	−6·5	14	77·5	−5·0	−4·0
93·1	2	22	−2·3	−5·5	−8	92·5	0·6	5·6
115·9	21	26	20·5	13·5	−4	117·4	−1·5	−2·1
83·8	1	34	−11·6	−6·5	4	83·7	0·1	1·6
113·3	11	12	17·9	3·5	−18	111·6	1·7	1·6
109·4	10	12	14·0	2·5	−18	110·1	−0·7	−2·4
$\Sigma Y =$	$\Sigma X_1 =$	$\Sigma X_2 =$	$\Sigma(Y - \overline{Y})$	$\Sigma(X_1 - \overline{X}_1)$	$\Sigma(X_2 - \overline{X}_2)$		$\Sigma e^2 =$	$\Sigma \Delta e^2 =$
1240·5	97	626	$= 0$	$= 0$	$= 0$		62·8	116·8

$d = 1·8$

$M = 13,$

$\overline{Y} = 95·4, \quad \overline{X}_1 = 7·5, \quad \overline{X}_2 = 30·0.$

$\Sigma(Y - \overline{Y})^2 = 2773,$

$\Sigma(X_1 - \overline{X}_1)(Y - \overline{Y}) = 730·5, \quad \Sigma(X_1 - \overline{X}_1)^2 = 307·75,$

$\Sigma(X_2 - \overline{X}_2)(Y - \overline{Y}) = -2472·7, \quad \Sigma(X_2 - \overline{X}_2)(X_1 - \overline{X}_1) = -305·0,$

$\Sigma(X_2 - \overline{X}_2)^2 = 3362.$

$b_1 = 1·440, \quad b_2 = -0·614,$

$a = \overline{Y} - b_1\overline{X}_1 - b_2\overline{X}_2 = 103·097$

since $(y - \overline{y}) = b_1(x_1 - \overline{X}_1) + b_2(x_2 - \overline{X}_2),$

so that finally

$$y = a + b_1 x_1 + b_2 x_2,$$

that is
$$y = 103\cdot097 + 1\cdot440\, x_1 - 0\cdot614\, x_2.$$

The definitions of all our statistics are extended in a similar way.

$$s^2 = \frac{\Sigma(Y - \overline{Y})^2 - b_1\Sigma(X_1 - \overline{X}_1)(Y - \overline{Y}) - b_2\Sigma(X_2 - \overline{X}_2)(Y - \overline{Y})}{M - 3}, \tag{2.7.1}$$

$$R_1^2 = \frac{b_1\Sigma(X_1 - \overline{X}_1)(Y - \overline{Y}) + b_2\Sigma(X_2 - \overline{X}_2)(Y - \overline{Y})}{\Sigma(Y - \overline{Y})^2} = R_2^2, \tag{2.7.2}$$

$$\mathrm{se}(b_1) = \sqrt{\left[\frac{s^2\Sigma(X_2 - \overline{X}_2)^2}{M\Sigma(X_1 - \overline{X}_1)^2\,\Sigma(X_2 - \overline{X}_2)^2 - \{\Sigma(X_1 - \overline{X}_1)(X_2 - \overline{X}_2)\}^2}\right]}, \tag{2.7.3}$$

$$\mathrm{se}(b_2) = \sqrt{\left[\frac{s^2\Sigma(X_1 - \overline{X}_1)^2}{M\Sigma(X_1 - \overline{X}_1)^2\,\Sigma(X_2 - \overline{X}_2)^2 - \{\Sigma(X_1 - \overline{X}_1)(X_2 - \overline{X}_2)\}^2}\right]}, \tag{2.7.4}$$

$$t_1 = b_1/\mathrm{se}(b_1), \tag{2.7.5}$$

and
$$t_2 = b_2/\mathrm{se}(b_2), \tag{2.7.6}$$

The calculated values of y are

$$y_i = (\overline{Y} - b_1\overline{X}_1 - b_2\overline{X}_2) + b_1 x_{i1} + b_2 x_{i2}, \tag{2.7.7}$$

for $i = 1, 2, \ldots, M$. The residuals are $e_i = Y_i - y_i$, where Y_i is the observed value and y_i the calculated value of y at $x_{1i} = X_{1i}$, $x_{2i} = X_{2i}$.

Durbin-Watson's d-statistic is

$$d = \frac{\displaystyle\sum_{i=2}^{M}(e_i - e_{i-1})^2}{\displaystyle\sum_{i=1}^{M} e_i^2} \tag{2.7.8}$$

This is calculated by forming the two further columns for e_i and $e_i - e_{i-1}$, and then accumulating the sums

$$\Sigma(e_i - e_{i-1})^2 \quad \text{and} \quad \Sigma e_i^2$$

Check that
$$\frac{\Sigma e_i^2}{M - 3} \simeq s^2. \tag{2.7.9}$$

§2.8 Multiple regression in N variables

The argument proceeds in exactly the same way for an N dimensional regression, except that it is now best expressed in matrix notation.

The normal equations are found to be

75

$$\Sigma Y - aM - b_1\Sigma X_1 - b_2\Sigma X_2 \ldots - b_N\Sigma X_N = 0$$

$$\Sigma X_1 Y - a\Sigma X_1 - b_1\Sigma Y_1^2 - b_2\Sigma X_1 X_2 \ldots - b_N\Sigma X_1 X_N = 0$$

$$\ldots\ldots$$

$$\Sigma X_N Y - a\Sigma X_N - b_1\Sigma X_N X_1 - b_2\Sigma X_N X_2 \ldots - b_N\Sigma X_N^2 = 0 \qquad (2.8.1)$$

where summation is from 1 to M throughout.

If we write b_0 for a, and introduce a dummy variable X_0, which always takes the value 1, into every observation, the above equations become

$$\Sigma X_0 Y - b_0\Sigma X_0^2 - b_1\Sigma X_0 X_1 - b_2\Sigma X_0 X_2 \ldots - b_N\Sigma X_0 X_N = 0$$

$$\Sigma X_1 Y - b_0\Sigma X_1 X_0 - b_1\Sigma X_1^2 - b_2\Sigma X_1 X_2 \ldots - b_N\Sigma X_1 X_N = 0$$

$$\ldots\ldots$$

$$\Sigma X_N Y - b_0\Sigma X_N X_0 - b_1\Sigma X_N X_1 - b_2\Sigma X_N X_2 \ldots - b_N\Sigma X_N^2 = 0, \qquad (2.8.2)$$

and these equations are readily expressed in matrix notation.

Let X be the data matrix with M rows and N columns, that is

$$X = \begin{bmatrix} X_{10} & X_{11} & X_{12} & \ldots & X_{1N} \\ X_{20} & X_{21} & X_{22} & \ldots & X_{2N} \\ & & \ldots\ldots & & \\ X_{M0} & X_{M1} & X_{M2} & \ldots & X_{MN} \end{bmatrix} \qquad (2.8.3)$$

Let y be the vector with M elements

$$y = \{Y_1, Y_2, \ldots, Y_M\}, \qquad (2.8.4)$$

and let b be the vector with $N + 1$ elements

$$b = \{b_0, b_1, b_2, \ldots, b_N\}, \qquad (2.8.5)$$

Then $X'X$ is the $(N + 1) \times (N + 1)$ matrix formed by multiplying X by its transpose X'. That is

$$X'X = \begin{bmatrix} \sum_{i=1}^{M} X_0^2 & \sum_{i=1}^{M} X_0 X_1 & \sum_{i=1}^{M} X_0 X_2 & \ldots & \sum_{i=1}^{M} X_0 X_N \\ \sum_{i=1}^{M} X_1 X_0 & \sum_{i=1}^{M} X_1^2 & & \ldots & \ldots \\ & & \ldots\ldots & & \\ \sum_{i=1}^{M} X_N X_0 & \sum_{i=1}^{M} X_N X_1 & \ldots & \ldots & \sum_{i=1}^{M} X_N^2 \end{bmatrix} \qquad (2.8.6)$$

This matrix contains all the sums of squares down the diagonal and every possible cross-product elsewhere. $X'y$ is the vector with $(N + 1)$ elements formed by multiplying the transposed matrix X' by the column vector y. That is

$$X'y = \left\{ \sum_{i=1}^{M} X_0 Y, \ \sum_{i=1}^{M} X_1 Y, \ \ldots, \ \ldots, \ \sum_{i=1}^{M} X_N Y \right\} \qquad (2.8.7)$$

The above normal equations (2.8.2) can now be rewritten most concisely in this matrix notation as

$$X'y = bX'X \tag{2.8.8}$$

where b is the required vector of solutions,

that is
$$b = \{b_0, b_1, \ldots, b_N\}$$

Let the inverse matrix $(X'X)^{-1}$ be denoted by $[c_{ij}] (i, j = 0, 1, 2, \ldots, N)$, then

$$b = (X'X)^{-1}X'y = [c_{ij}]X'y \tag{2.8.9}$$

Thus the b's which we are trying to calculate are given by

$$b_v = c_{v0}\sum_{i=1}^{M} X_{0i} Y_i + c_{v1}\sum_{i=1}^{M} X_{1i} Y_i + \ldots + c_{vN}\sum_{i=1}^{M} X_{Ni} Y_i , \tag{2.8.10}$$

for $v = 0, 1, 2, \ldots, N$.

The various statistics can all be generalized in the matrix notation, thus:

$$s^2 = \frac{\left(\sum_{i=1}^{M} Y_i^2\right) - b'X'y}{M - N - 1} , \tag{2.8.11}$$

$$R_1^2 = b'X'y \Big/ \left(\sum_{i=1}^{M} Y_i^2\right) , \tag{2.8.12}$$

$$R_2^2 = 1 - \frac{\Sigma Y^2 - b'X'y}{\Sigma Y^2 - (\Sigma Y)^2/M} , \tag{2.8.13}$$

$$\{se(b_j)\} = [\sqrt{(\text{tr}\{s^2[c_{ij}]\})}] , \tag{2.8.14}$$

$$[(N + 1) \text{ elements}, j = 0, 1, 2, \ldots, N]$$

that is, the square root of each diagonal element of the variance matrix,

$$V(b) = s^2(X'X)^{-1} = s^2[c_{ij}], \tag{2.8.15}$$

$$\{t_j\} = \{b_j/se(b_j)\}, \quad [(N + 1) \text{ elements}] \tag{2.8.16}$$

$$\{y_i\} = \left\{\sum_{j=1}^{N} b_j X_{ij}\right\}, \quad (M \text{ elements}, i = 1, 2, \ldots, M) \tag{2.8.17}$$

$$\{e_i\} = \{Y_i - y_i\}, \quad (M \text{ elements}) \tag{2.8.18}$$

and
$$d = \frac{\sum_{i=1}^{M} (e_i - e_{i-1})}{\sum_{i=1}^{M} e_i^2} , \quad \text{as always} \tag{2.8.19}$$

If we are attempting such a calculation on hand-machines, the size of the matrix $X'X$ which we have to invert, can always be reduced by 1, by transferring the origin of our data to its arithmetic means, as we have seen in the one and two dimensional cases worked out in full in our examples. But, if it is at all possible, it is best to use automatic computing methods for regressions involving more than two independent variables.

§2.9 Layout of multiple regressions for automatic computation

The original data usually comes to the computer as a set of M rows of data, each row containing say h elements,

$$
\begin{array}{ccccc}
a_{11} & a_{12} & a_{13} & \cdots & a_{1h} \\
a_{21} & a_{22} & a_{23} & \cdots & a_{2h} \\
& & \cdots\cdots & & \\
a_{M1} & a_{M2} & a_{M3} & \cdots & a_{Mh}
\end{array}
$$

This, the main data, can be prepared in rows (or columns), as the main input tape. This input tape for the computer should be preceded by a title, and followed by some groups of code numbers, one group for each regression required, to give the computer precise instructions as to the types of regression to be performed, and the exact transformations to be made of the input data before the start of the actual regression.

The machine having read the input data, and sent this to auxiliary storage, the program then reads the first set of code numbers and brings out the input data from the auxiliary store one row at a time. When it has read one row of the data, the computer makes the transformation of the data called for by the code numbers. Thus it may take $\log_e a$ of the first k numbers read, treat the next l numbers as plain, form exponentials e^a, ... of the next m numbers, and take first differences or reciprocals, or any combinations of these, such as first differences of $\log_e a$, or reciprocals of e^a. The machine is then holding in its store a row of transformed data. From this it selects the element to be treated as the weight w, if we are performing a weighted regression, or selects $w \equiv 1$, a unit, if we are doing a plain regression. The machine then places this value of w as the first item of data in the final sequence. Next it selects the Y of the regression and places this second in the sequence. Then it selects the X's and places them in the order in this data sequence, including $X_0 \equiv 1$, for the constant immediately after the Y if required.

Thus from our initial row of data

$$ a_{11}, \ a_{12}, \ \ldots, \ a_{1h}, $$

we have made various simple transformations and selected $N + 3$ elements which we have arranged in a row as a vector

$$ D_1 \ = \ \{w_1, \ Y_1, \ X_{01}, \ X_{11}, \ X_{21}, \ \ldots, \ X_{N1}\} \tag{2.9.1} $$

Next we add the cross product $D'D$ of the above row of final data into the matrix

$$
\begin{bmatrix}
\Sigma wY^2 & \Sigma wY & \Sigma wX_1 Y & \Sigma wX_2 Y & \cdots & \Sigma wX_N Y \\
& \Sigma w & \Sigma wX_1 & \Sigma wX_2 & \cdots & \Sigma wX_N \\
& & \Sigma wX_1^2 & \Sigma wX_1 X_2 & \cdots & \Sigma wX_1 X_N \\
& & \cdots & \cdots & \cdots & \cdots \\
& & & & & \Sigma wX_N^2
\end{bmatrix} \tag{2.9.2}
$$

accumulating each cross product of elements on to the sums as each row of data is formed. Here all the summations are of M items each. This matrix is of size $(N + 2) \times (N + 2)$ but it is symmetric. Hence it is only necessary to store the upper triangle of the matrix containing $\frac{1}{2}(N + 2) \times (N + 3)$ elements in all. Every number required in our calculations, except N and M, is contained in this matrix, which we will call the 'master' matrix of the regression. This master matrix can now go to auxiliary storage, if the computer being used has a small high speed store.

Next in accordance with the initial code numbers, the machine selects from the master matrix, the matrix $X'X$, and the vector $X'y$ which are to be used in the particular regression required.

There are many possible choices at this stage. For example, we may want a regression on all the variables available including the constant, that is, based on the equation

$$Y = b_0 + b_1 X_1 + b_2 X_2 + \ldots + b_N X_N. \tag{2.9.3}$$

Then $X'X$ would be the $(N + 1) \times (N + 1)$ matrix.

$$X'X = \begin{bmatrix} \Sigma w & \Sigma w X_1 & \Sigma w X_2 & \ldots & \Sigma w X_N \\ & \Sigma w X_1^2 & \Sigma w X_1 X_2 & \ldots & \Sigma w X_1 X_N \\ & & \ldots & \ldots & \ldots \\ & & & & \Sigma w X_N^2 \end{bmatrix} \tag{2.9.4}$$

and $X'y$ would be the vector

$$X'y = \{\Sigma w Y, \ \Sigma w X_1 Y, \ \Sigma w X_2 Y, \ \ldots \ \Sigma w X_N Y\}, \tag{2.9.5}$$

with $N + 1$ elements.

Alternatively we migh call for regression without constant, in which case the machine would select the $N \times N$ matrix

$$X'X = \begin{bmatrix} \Sigma w X_1^2 & \Sigma w X_1 X_2 & \ldots & \Sigma w X_1 X_N \\ & \Sigma w X_2^2 & \ldots & \Sigma w X_2 X_N \\ & & \ldots & \ldots \\ & & & \Sigma w X_N^2 \end{bmatrix}, \tag{2.9.6}$$

and the vector $X'y = \{\Sigma w X_1 Y, \ \Sigma w X_2 Y, \ \ldots, \ \Sigma w X_N Y\}$. $\hspace{1cm}$ (2.9.7)

Again we may want successive sets of regression, introducing an extra X at each stage, based on the set of equations

$$Y = b_0 + b_1 X_1$$
$$Y = b_0 + b_1 X_1 + b_2 X_2$$
$$Y = b_0 + b_1 X_1 + b_2 X_2 + b_3 X_3$$
$$\cdots$$
$$Y = b_0 + b_1 X_1 + b_2 X_2 + \ldots + b_N X_N. \tag{2.9.8}$$

After one particular matrix $X'X$ and its corresponding vector $X'y$ have been selected from the master matrix, $(X'X)^{-1}$ is formed on top of $X'X$ by the Jourdan process outlined in paragraph 1.3. Then $b'X'y$ is formed and stored, and the three quantities

$$s^2, \quad R_1^2, \quad \text{and} \quad R_2^2 \quad \text{are printed.}$$

Next $(X'X)^{-1}$ is multiplied by s^2, to form $V(b)$ and, provided that it is really of interest, $V(b)$ can be printed out at this point, though, if a large number of regressions are being performed or if N is at all large, it is best to avoid wasting the machine-time necessary to print out all the elements of $V(b)$.

Then $\{se(b_j)\}$ and $\{t_j\}$ are formed and printed.

Note, $\{se(b_j)\}$ should be formed as $\{\sqrt{|s^2 c_{jj}|}\}$ since if s^2 or c_{jj} is very small and nearly zero, $s^2 c_{jj}$ may appear as a small negative number within the machine.

Then, if the residuals are required, the final data is brought down from the auxiliary store, one row at a time to re-form the vector

$$D = \{w, \; Y, \; X_1, \; X_2, \; ..., \; X_N\}$$

and to calculate $\{y_i\}$ and $\{e_i\}$. The sums Σe_i^2 and $\Sigma(e_{i+1} - e_i)^2$ are accumulated. Again these vectors need not be printed unless they are needed. Finally, the d-statistic is printed, and the calculation goes on either to perform a new regression with a different equation on the same main data, or to read in an entirely new set of data and code numbers.

SECTION 2

A GENERAL REGRESSION PROGRAM

§2.10 Specification of program REGX

This program is intended for general use as a multi-purpose regression routine. The name of the program is REGX. It uses about 12000 words of store, one input channel for tape, one line printer for output and no magnetic tape units.

The first section reads in the main data tape, arranges the data in rows in the store, and checks that the tape is in the correct layout.

Layout of main data tape

n	code no. of data.
0 or 1	for data punched in rows or in columns, 0 or 1, integer,
hm	h items per row, m rows, $hm < 2000$, h, m as integers,
main data	punched either as h variables per row, m rows, or as m observations per column, h columns,
-1	symbol to terminate data.

80

If any of the three heading numbers 0, 1, h, and m, are incorrect, that is if the second number is not 0 or 1, or if either h or m is $\leqslant 0$, the program prints "FAULTY CODE DIGIT" and waits ready to re-read more main data.

If there are not hm items in the main data or if -1 is left off the end, the program prints "FAULTY CODE DIGIT" and waits ready to re-read more main data.

The program next reads one control tape, and checks that its layout is correct.

Layout of control tapes

h	code no. of control tape.
	0 = no action 1 = print residues, 2 = print expected values, 3 = print both
	0 = no action 1 = remove means
P	$P\%$ level for significance of t_i's (mainly to vary amount of printing required).
k	the number of x's in the regression (including constant term), k punched as an integer.
$k + 2$	groups of four digits each, for w, y, and kx's, where $k \leqslant 12$.
-1	at end to go back, ready to read another control tape, to perform another regression on the same set of main data, or
-1	at end, to go back ready to read in another set of main data, and
-1	its control tapes.

If the second number read on the control tape is not 0 or 1 the program prints "CONTROL FAULT" and waits ready to read another control tape. If there are not $k + 2$ groups of 4 digits each on the control tape, or if there is no -1 when $k + 2$ groups have been read, the program prints "NO -1 ON END" and waits ready to read another control tape.

The second part of the program builds up the data for the particular regression, from the main data and the group of $4(k + 2)$ control digits. The 4 digits in each group are interpreted according to the following scheme.

Let the main data be in the store in rows as

$$
\begin{array}{cccc}
a_{00} & a_{01} & \cdots & a_{0,h-1} \\
a_{10} & a_{11} & \cdots & a_{1,h-1} \\
& & \cdots\cdots & \\
a_{m-1,0} & a_{m-1,1} & \cdots & a_{m-1,h-1}
\end{array}
$$

Then the first group of 4 digits forms w, the second group of 4 digits forms y and the remaining k groups of 4 digits each form $x_0, x_1, \ldots x_{k-1}$, respectively.

The first digit of each group V_1, selects an $a_{uv}(v = 1, 2, \ldots, k)$ as z_1, the second digit V_2, selects an a_{uv} as z_2.

The third digit V_3 can be 0, 1, 2, $\ldots$ 9, 10, 11, or 12 and forms $f(z_1, z_2)$ where

$$0 \quad \text{is the null transform } z_1' = z_1,$$

$$1 \quad \text{is } z_1' = z_1 + z_2,$$

$$2 \quad \text{is } z_1' = z_1 - z_2,$$

$$3 \quad \text{is } z_1' = z_1 \times z_2,$$

$$4 \quad \text{is } z_1' = z_1/z_2,$$

$$5 \quad \text{is } z_1' = \log_e z_1,$$

$$6 \quad \text{is } z_1' = \exp z_1,$$

$$7 \quad \text{is } z_1' = z_1^2,$$

$$8 \quad \text{is } z_1 = 1/z_1,$$

$$9 \quad \text{is } z_1' = \log_e^2 z_1,$$

$$10 \quad \text{is } z_1' = \text{difference } z_1, \text{ i.e. } a_{u+1,v} - a_{uv} = z_1',$$

$$11 \quad \text{is } z_1' = 1,$$

$$12 \quad \text{is } z_1' = t \quad (\text{time trend})$$

The fourth digit V_4 has a similar sequence of transforms except that now the transformation is performed on z_1' and z_2, instead of on z_1 and z_2.

Other transforms can be inserted in the program at this point using higher digits 13, 14, ... to indicate them.

As each row of data is formed as

$$w_u \, y_u \, x_{u1} \, x_{u2} \; \cdots \; x_{uk-1},$$

(where $w_u \equiv 1$ for plain regressions), it is accumulated into the symmetric $k \times k$ matrix

$$
\begin{bmatrix}
\sum_{u=0}^{m-1} w_u x_{u0}^2 & \sum_{u=0}^{m-1} w_u x_{u0} \, x_{u1} & \cdots & \sum_{u=0}^{m-1} w_u x_{u0} \, x_{u,k-1} \\
 & \sum_{u=0}^{m-1} w_u x_{u1}^2 & \cdots & \sum_{u=0}^{m-1} w_u x_{u1} \, x_{u,k-1} \\
 & \cdots & \cdots & \cdots \\
 & & & \sum_{u=0}^{m-1} w_u x_{u,k-1}^2
\end{bmatrix} = X'X
$$

the vector of k elements

$$\left\{ \sum_{u=0}^{m-1} w_u y_u \quad \sum_{u=0}^{m-1} w_u y_u x_{u1} \quad \cdots \quad \sum_{u=0}^{m-1} w_u y_u x_{u,k-1} \right\} = X'y$$

and the quantities

$$\sum_{u=0}^{m-1} 1 = m, \quad \sum_{u=0}^{m-1} w_u, \quad \sum_{u=0}^{m-1} w_u y_u, \quad \text{and} \quad \sum_{u=0}^{m-1} w_u y_u^2 .$$

If the control digit $P = 0$, the transformed data is printed as it is formed.

When all the data has been selected and $X'X$, $X'y$ etc. formed, $X'X$ is inverted to give $(X'X)^{-1}$ in the store.

Then the vector of k elements $\{b_i\}$, $i = 1, 2, ..., k$, is calculated from the equation

$$\{b_i\} = (X'X)^{-1}X'y.$$

The vector $\{b_i\}$ is printed, together with the three statistics

$$s^2 = \frac{\Sigma wy^2 - \{b\}' X'y}{(m-k)}$$

$$R_1^2 = \{b_i\}'X'y/\Sigma wy^2,$$

$$R_2^2 = 1 + \frac{\Sigma wy^2 - \{b_i\}'X'y}{(\Sigma wy)^2/\Sigma w - \Sigma wy^2}$$

and the vector
$$\{se(b_i)\},$$

where
$$se(b_i) = \sqrt{|var\ b_i|}$$

that is the square root of the diagonal elements of the variance matrix

$$V(b) = s^2(X'X)^{-1}.$$

The vector $\{t_i\}$ is formed where $t_i = b_i/se(b_i)$. If $|t_i| > P$, the percentage level of significance on the control tape, for any $i = 1, 2, \ldots, k$, the results are deemed of some significance, and these further items are printed: $\{t_i\}$, m, k, Σw, Σwy, Σwy^2, $X'y$, and the triangular matrix $V(b)$. This extra printing always takes place if $P = 0$. The Durban-Watson d-statistic is defined as

$$d = \sum_{r=1}^{m-1} (\Delta e_r)^2 \Big/ \sum_{r=0}^{m-1} e_r^2 ,$$

where $\Delta e_r \equiv e_r - e_{r-1}$, and e_r is the residual $Y_r - y_r$, where y_r is the input value of y, and Y_r is the expected value of the dependent variable, that is $Y_r = X'\{b_i\}$, the value of y calculated in the machine.

If printing of residuals or expected values is called for, on the control tape, the machine further prints e_r, Y_r, for $r = 1, 2, \ldots, m$, and finally d. It then pauses at 2, ready to read in further control tapes or to read $-1\ -1$ to return it to pause 1, ready to read in more main data.

§2.11 Example of the use of REGX

Layout of main data tape

	99	code no. of data
	0	data is in rows
5	25	5 items per row, 25 rows. Check $5 \times 25 < 2000$.
		main data

y_{11} y_{12} x_{11} x_{12} x_{13}

y_{21} y_{22} x_{21} x_{22} x_{23}

. . . . .

$y_{25,1}$ $y_{25,2}$ $x_{25,1}$ $x_{25,2}$ $x_{25,3}$

-1

			991	code no. of 1st control.
1	0	5	3	First equation to be fitted is
				$y_1 = a + b_1 x_1 + b_2 \log_e x_2,$
0	0	11	0	weight is $\equiv 1$,
1	0	0	0	y_1 is first column of data,
0	0	11	0	constant $x_0 \equiv 1$,
3	0	0	0	x_1 is third column of data,
4	0	5	0	x_2 is $\log_e$ of fourth column of data,
−1				

			992	
1	1	5	1	Second equation is
1	0	0	0	$\log_e y_2 = a + b_1 \log_e (x_1 + x_2)$
2	0	5	0	with y_1 used as a weight
3	4	1	5	and means removed from data,
−1				to stop run.
−1				

§2.12 Flow diagram for REGX

Program REGX, master routine.
Read and check main data in rows or in columns.

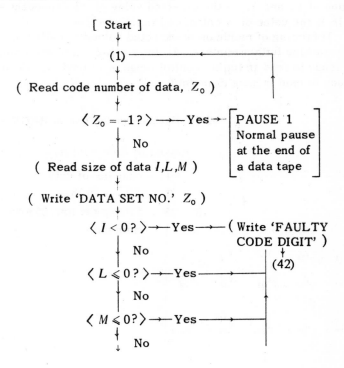

84

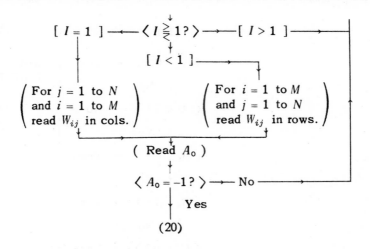

$[\,I = 1\,]$ ——— $\langle\, I \gtreqless 1? \,\rangle$ ——— $[\,I > 1\,]$ ———

$[\,I < 1\,]$ ———

$\begin{pmatrix} \text{For } j = 1 \text{ to } N \\ \text{and } i = 1 \text{ to } M \\ \text{read } W_{ij} \text{ in cols.} \end{pmatrix}$ $\begin{pmatrix} \text{For } i = 1 \text{ to } M \\ \text{and } j = 1 \text{ to } N \\ \text{read } W_{ij} \text{ in rows.} \end{pmatrix}$

(Read A_0)

$\langle\, A_0 = -1? \,\rangle$ ——— No ———

Yes

(20)

REGX. Master. Read and check control data.

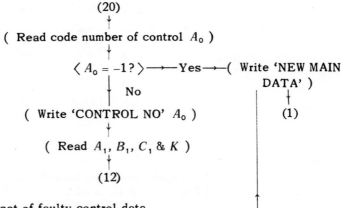

(20)

(Read code number of control A_0)

$\langle\, A_0 = -1? \,\rangle$ ———Yes——(Write 'NEW MAIN DATA')

No

(Write 'CONTROL NO' A_0)

(1)

(Read $A_1, B_1, C_1, \& K$)

(12)

Read and ignore one set of faulty control data.

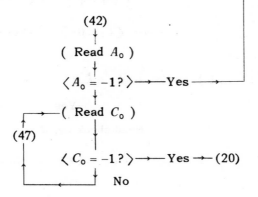

(42)

(Read A_0)

$\langle\, A_0 = -1? \,\rangle$ ———Yes———

(Read C_0)

(47)

$\langle\, C_0 = -1? \,\rangle$ ———Yes——(20)

No

REGX. Master. Check control digits.

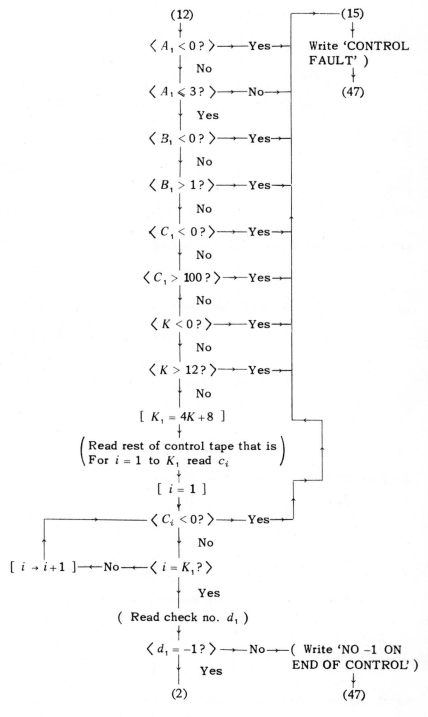

(12)

$\langle A_1 < 0 ? \rangle$ ——Yes→ (15)

    No   Write 'CONTROL FAULT')

$\langle A_1 \leqslant 3 ? \rangle$ ——No→ (47)

    Yes

$\langle B_1 < 0 ? \rangle$ ——Yes→

    No

$\langle B_1 > 1 ? \rangle$ ——Yes→

    No

$\langle C_1 < 0 ? \rangle$ ——Yes→

    No

$\langle C_1 > 100 ? \rangle$ ——Yes→

    No

$\langle K < 0 ? \rangle$ ——Yes→

    No

$\langle K > 12 ? \rangle$ ——Yes→

    No

$[\ K_1 = 4K + 8\ ]$

$\left(\begin{array}{l} \text{Read rest of control tape that is} \\ \text{For } i = 1 \text{ to } K_1 \text{ read } c_i \end{array} \right)$

$[\ i = 1\ ]$

$\langle C_i < 0 ? \rangle$ ——Yes→

    No

$[\ i \to i+1\ ]$——No——$\langle i = K_1 ? \rangle$

    Yes

(Read check no. d_1)

$\langle d_1 = -1 ? \rangle$ ——No——(Write 'NO –1 ON END OF CONTROL')

    Yes (47)

(2)

REGX. Master. Clear working sequences and start first data cycle.

(2)

↓

[For $i = 1$ to 144, $a_i = 0$, & $b_i = 0$]

↓

[$d_s = e_s = 0$]

↓

[$m' = m$, $k' = k$]

↓

[For $i = 1$ to 15, $d_i = x_i = y_i = z_i = 0$]

↓

[$V = 0$]

↓

(15)←[$c_1 < 0$]←←⟨ $c_1 \lesseqgtr 0$? ⟩→→[$c_1 > 0$]→┐

↓ [$c_1 = 0$]

(Write 'TRANSFORMED DATA IS')

↓

(15)←←[$b_1 < 0$]←←⟨ $b_1 \lesseqgtr 0$? ⟩→→[$b_1 = 0$]→→(5)

↓ [$b_1 > 0$]

[$k' = k + 1$]

↓

[$j = 1$]

↓

[subroutine DATA]

↓

[$x_1' = x_1 + z_2$]

↓

[$k_1 = k + 2$]

↓

$$\begin{bmatrix} \text{For } i = 2 \text{ to } k_1, x_i \to x_i + z_{i+1}\, z_2 \\ \text{that is} \quad x_i = \sum_j w_j\, z_{i+1,j} \end{bmatrix}$$

↓

[$j \to j + 1$]←No←←⟨ $j = m$? ⟩

↓ Yes

(3)

REGX. Master. Form means, and start second data cycle.

(3)

↓

[$x_0 = 1/x_1$]

↓

[For $i = 2$ to $k_1, x_i \to x_i x_0$]

↓

[$j = 1$]

↓

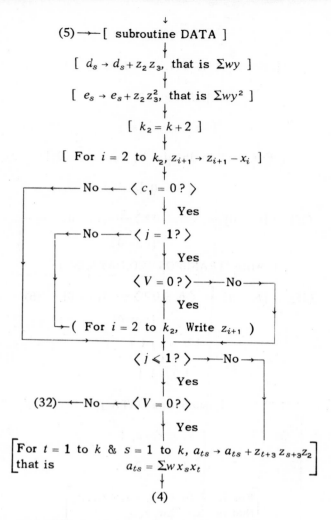

$(5) \longrightarrow [$ subroutine DATA $]$

$[\ d_s \to d_s + z_2 z_3,$ that is $\Sigma wy\ ]$

$[\ e_s \to e_s + z_2 z_3^2,$ that is $\Sigma wy^2\ ]$

$[\ k_2 = k + 2\ ]$

$[$ For $i = 2$ to $k_2, z_{i+1} \to z_{i+1} - x_i\ ]$

$\longleftarrow$ No $\longleftarrow \langle c_1 = 0?\rangle$

Yes

$\longleftarrow$ No $\longleftarrow \langle j = 1?\rangle$

Yes

$\langle V = 0?\rangle \longrightarrow$ No $\longrightarrow$

Yes

$\longleftarrow ($ For $i = 2$ to $k_2,$ Write $z_{i+1}\ )$

$\langle j \leqslant 1?\rangle \longrightarrow$ No $\longrightarrow$

Yes

$(32) \longleftarrow$ No $\longleftarrow \langle V = 0?\rangle$

Yes

$$\left[\begin{array}{l}\text{For } t = 1 \text{ to } k\ \&\ s = 1 \text{ to } k,\ a_{ts} \to a_{ts} + z_{t+3}\, z_{s+3} z_2 \\ \text{that is} \qquad\qquad a_{ts} = \Sigma w x_s x_t \end{array}\right]$$

(4)

REGX. Master. Form $X'y$ and invert $X'X$.

(4)

$[\ y_3' = y_3 + z_2$ that is $y_3 = \Sigma w\ ]$

$[\ y_4' = y_4 + z_2 z_3$ that is $y_4 = \Sigma wy\ ]$

$[\ k_1 = k + 1\ ]$

$$\left[\begin{array}{l}\text{For } i = 1 \text{ to } k_1,\ y_{i+4}' = y_{i+4} + z_2 z_3 z_{i+2} \\ \text{that is} \qquad\qquad y_{i+4} = \Sigma w x_i y \end{array}\right]$$

(32)

$$(32)$$
$$\downarrow$$
$$(5) \longleftarrow [\ j' = j+1\ ] \longleftarrow No \longleftarrow \langle\ j = m?\ \rangle$$
$$\downarrow\ \text{Yes}$$
$$\langle\ c_1 = 0?\ \rangle \longrightarrow No \longrightarrow$$
$$\downarrow\ \text{Yes}$$
$$(\ \text{Write 'XX = '}\ )$$
$$\downarrow$$
$$(\ \text{For } i = 1 \text{ to } k,\ \&\ j = 1 \text{ to } i,\ \text{write } a_{ij}\ )$$
$$\downarrow$$
$$[\ \text{Subroutine INVERT}\ ]$$
$$\downarrow$$
$$\langle\ k = 0?\ \rangle \longrightarrow \text{Yes} \longrightarrow (20)$$
$$\downarrow\ \text{No}$$
$$(6)$$

REGX. Master. Form and print b vector.

$$(6)$$
$$\downarrow$$
$$[\ t = 1\ ]$$
$$\downarrow$$
$$[\ a_{t+2} = 0\ ]$$
$$\downarrow$$
$$[\ \text{For } s = 1 \text{ to } k,\ a_{t+2} \to a_{t+2} + b_{t,s}\, y_{s+5}\ ]$$
$$\downarrow$$
$$[\ t \to t+1\ ] \longleftarrow No \longleftarrow \langle\ t = k?\ \rangle$$
$$\downarrow\ \text{Yes}$$
$$(\ \text{For } t = 1 \text{ to } k,\ \text{Write 'B =', } a_{t+2}\ )$$
$$\downarrow$$
$$[\ a_2 = 0\ ]$$
$$\downarrow$$
$$[\ \text{For } s = 1 \text{ to } k,\ a_2 \to a_2 + a_{s+2}\, y_{s+5}\ ]$$
$$\downarrow$$
$$[\ e_1 = x_2\ ]$$
$$\downarrow$$
$$[\ \text{For } i = 1 \text{ to } k,\ e_1 \to e_1 - a_{i+2}\, x_{i+2}\ ]$$
$$\downarrow$$
$$[\ f_1 = 0\ ]$$
$$\downarrow$$
$$\langle\ m' - k' = 0?\ \rangle \longrightarrow \text{Yes} \longrightarrow$$
$$\downarrow\ \text{No}$$

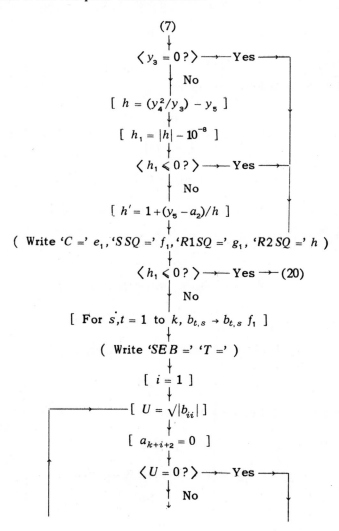

$$[\ f_1 = (y_5 - a_2)/(m' - k')\ ]$$

$$[\ g_1 = 0\ ]$$

$$\langle\, y_5 = 0\,?\,\rangle \longrightarrow \text{Yes} \longrightarrow$$

No

$$[\ g_1 = a_2/y_5\ ]$$

$$[\ h = 0\ ]$$

$$(7)$$

REGX. Master. Form and print other statistics

$$(7)$$

$$\langle\, y_3 = 0\,?\,\rangle \longrightarrow \text{Yes} \longrightarrow$$

No

$$[\ h = (y_4^2/y_3) - y_5\ ]$$

$$[\ h_1 = |h| - 10^{-8}\ ]$$

$$\langle\, h_1 \leqslant 0\,?\,\rangle \longrightarrow \text{Yes} \longrightarrow$$

No

$$[\ h' = 1 + (y_5 - a_2)/h\ ]$$

$$(\ \text{Write } \text{'}C =\text{'}\ e_1,\ \text{'}SSQ =\text{'}\ f_1,\ \text{'}R1SQ =\text{'}\ g_1,\ \text{'}R2SQ =\text{'}\ h\ )$$

$$\langle\, h_1 < 0\,?\,\rangle \longrightarrow \text{Yes} \longrightarrow (20)$$

No

$$[\ \text{For } \dot{s}, t = 1 \text{ to } k,\ b_{t,s} \rightarrow b_{t,s}\, f_1\ ]$$

$$(\ \text{Write } \text{'}SEB =\text{'}\ \text{'}T =\text{'}\ )$$

$$[\ i = 1\ ]$$

$$[\ U = \sqrt{|b_{ii}|}\ ]$$

$$[\ a_{k+i+2} = 0\ ]$$

$$\langle\, U = 0\,?\,\rangle \longrightarrow \text{Yes} \longrightarrow$$

No

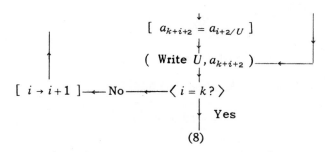

$$[\ a_{k+i+2} = a_{i+2/U}\ ]$$

$$(\ \text{Write}\ U, a_{k+i+2}\ )$$

$$[\ i \to i+1\ ]\longleftarrow\text{No}\longleftarrow\langle\ i = k\,?\ \rangle$$

Yes

(8)

REGX, Master. Extra printing

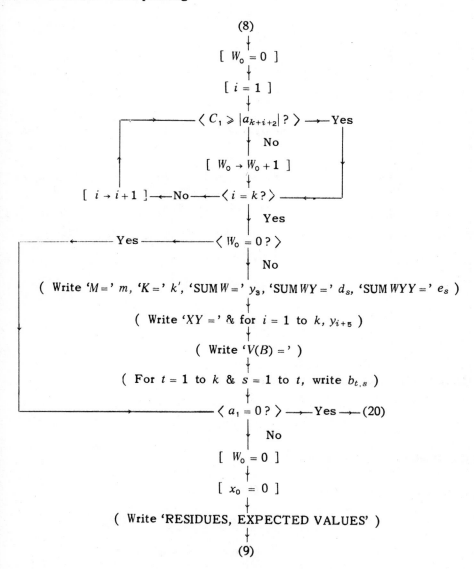

(8)

$$[\ W_0 = 0\ ]$$

$$[\ i = 1\ ]$$

$$\langle\ C_1 \geqslant |a_{k+i+2}|\,?\ \rangle\longrightarrow\text{Yes}$$

No

$$[\ W_0 \to W_0 + 1\ ]$$

$$[\ i \to i+1\ ]\longleftarrow\text{No}\longleftarrow\langle\ i = k\,?\ \rangle$$

Yes

$$\text{Yes}\longleftarrow\langle\ W_0 = 0\,?\ \rangle$$

No

$$(\ \text{Write}\ 'M=\text{'}\ m,\ 'K=\text{'}\ k',\ '\text{SUM}\ W=\text{'}\ y_3,\ '\text{SUM}\ WY=\text{'}\ d_s,\ '\text{SUM}\ WYY=\text{'}\ e_s\ )$$

$$(\ \text{Write}\ 'XY =\text{'}\ \&\ \text{for}\ i = 1\ \text{to}\ k,\ y_{i+5}\ )$$

$$(\ \text{Write}\ 'V(B) =\text{'}\ )$$

$$(\ \text{For}\ t = 1\ \text{to}\ k\ \&\ s = 1\ \text{to}\ t,\ \text{write}\ b_{t,s}\ )$$

$$\langle\ a_1 = 0\,?\ \rangle\longrightarrow\text{Yes}\longrightarrow(20)$$

No

$$[\ W_0 = 0\ ]$$

$$[\ x_0 = 0\ ]$$

$$(\ \text{Write}\ '\text{RESIDUES, EXPECTED VALUES'}\ )$$

(9)

REGX. Master. Form residues, and expected values.

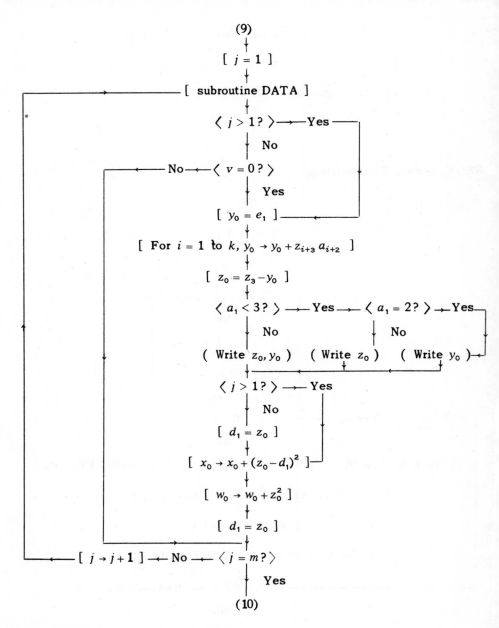

REGX. Master. Form d statistic.

(10)
$$[\ y_0 = 0\ ]$$
$$\langle\, w_0 = 0\,?\,\rangle \longrightarrow \text{Yes}$$

$$\downarrow \text{No}$$

$$[\ y_0 = x_0 / w_0\ ]$$

$$\downarrow$$

$$(\ \text{Write 'SUM}\,DE\,SQ =\text{'}\ x_0,\ \text{'SUM}\,ESQ =\text{'}\ w_0,\ \text{'END OF REG}\,DW =\text{'}\ y_0\ )$$

$$\downarrow$$

$$(20)$$

Subroutine INVERT. This subroutine is on the same lines as the inversion routine described in the first chapter.

Subroutine DATA. This subroutine sets up one row of transformed data in the Z sequence.

Copy one row of data from main data sequence W into the E sequence

$$[\ \text{Entry},\ l, j, k\ \text{and}\ m_d\ \text{set}\ ]$$

$$\downarrow$$

$$[\ z_1 = 1 \cdot 0\ ]$$

$$\downarrow$$

$$[\ e_r = W_{j,r}\ \text{for}\ r = 1,\ \text{to}\ l.\ ]$$

$$\downarrow$$

$$[\ k_1 = k + 2\ ]$$

$$\downarrow$$

$$[\ i = 1\ ]$$

$$\downarrow$$

$$(90)$$

Test code digits.

$$(90)$$

$$\downarrow$$

$$\langle\ c_{4i-2} = 0\,?\ \rangle \longrightarrow \text{No}$$

$$\downarrow \text{Yes}$$

$$[\ p = 1\ ]$$

$$\downarrow$$

$$[\ e_0 = e_p\ ]$$

$$\downarrow$$

$$\langle\ c_{4i-3} = 0\,?\ \rangle \longrightarrow \text{No}$$

$$\downarrow \text{Yes}$$

$$[\ p = 1\ ]$$

$$\downarrow$$

$$[\ f_0 = e_p\ ]$$

$$\downarrow$$

$$[\ q = c_{4i-1} + 1\ ]$$

$$\downarrow$$

$$(91)$$

93

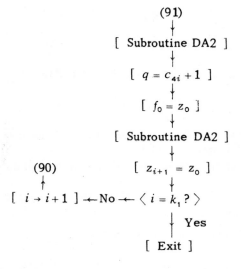

$$(91)$$
$$[\text{ Subroutine DA2 }]$$
$$[q = c_{4i} + 1]$$
$$[f_0 = z_0]$$
$$[\text{ Subroutine DA2 }]$$

$$(90)$$
$$[z_{i+1} = z_0]$$
$$[i \to i+1] \longleftarrow \text{No} \longleftarrow \langle i = k_1 ? \rangle$$
$$\downarrow \text{ Yes}$$
$$[\text{ Exit }]$$

Subroutine DA2. This subroutine sets up one item of transformed data, by a multiway switch.

$$[\text{ Entry, } i, j, q, e_0, f_0, m_d \text{ and } l \text{ set }]$$

$$\text{No} \leftarrow \langle q = \quad 1, \quad 2, \quad 3, \quad 4, \quad 5, \quad 6, \quad 7, \quad 8, \quad 9, \quad 10, \quad 11, \quad 12, \quad 13, \rangle$$

Yes (210)   (212)   (214)   (216)   (218)   (220)   (222)

(211)   (213)   (215)   (217)   (219)   (221)

$$(203)$$
$$[\text{ Exit }]$$

$$(210) \longrightarrow [z_0 = f_0] \longrightarrow (203)$$

$$(211) \longrightarrow [z_0 = e_0 + f_0] \longrightarrow (203)$$

$$(212) \longrightarrow [z_0 = f_0 - e_0] \longrightarrow (203)$$

$$(213) \longrightarrow [z_0 = e_0 f_0] \longrightarrow (203)$$

$$(214) \longrightarrow \langle e_0 = 0 ? \rangle \longrightarrow \text{Yes} \to (234)$$
$$\downarrow \text{ No}$$
$$[z_0 = f_0 / e_0]$$
$$(203)$$

$$(234) \longrightarrow (\text{ Write 'ZERO DIVISOR' }) \longrightarrow [z_0 = 10^8] \longrightarrow (203)$$

94

(215) ⟶ ⟨ $f_0 \leqslant 0$? ⟩ ⟶ Yes ⟶ (238)

↓ No

[$z_0 = \log_e(f_0)$]

↓

(203)

(216) ⟶ [$z_0 = e^{f_0}$] ⟶ (203)

(217) ⟶ [$z_0 = f_0^2$] ⟶ (203)

(218) ⟶ ⟨ $f_0 = 0$? ⟩ ⟶ Yes ⟶ (234)

↓ No

[$z_0 = 1/f_0$]

↓

(203)

(219) ⟶ ⟨ $f_0 > 0$? ⟩ ⟶ No ⟶ (238)

↓ Yes

[$z_0 = \log_e^2(f_0)$]

↓

(203)

(238) ⟶ (Write 'NEGATIVE LOG') ⟶ (203)

(220) ⟶ [$d_i = z_{i+1} + d_i$]

↓

[$z_0 = f_0 - d_i$]

↓

⟨ $j = 1$? ⟩ ⟶ No ⟶ (203)

↓ Yes

⟨ $v = 0$? ⟩ ⟶ No ⟶

↓ Yes

[$v = v+1$, $m_d = m-1$]

↓

[$z_2 = 0$]

↓

(203)

(222) ⟶ ⟨ $e_0 = 0$? ⟩ ⟶ Yes ⟶ (234)

↓ No

⟨ $f_0 = 0$? ⟩ ⟶ Yes ⟶ (234)

↓

$$\downarrow \text{No}$$
$$[\ z_0 = 1/(f_0 e_0)\ ]$$
$$\downarrow$$
$$(203)$$

$$(221) \longrightarrow [\ z_0 = 1\ ] \longrightarrow (203)$$

$$(223) \longrightarrow [\ z_0 = l\ ] \longrightarrow (203)$$

§2.13 Main Fortran Program REGX

```
      PROGRAM (REGX)
      INPUT 1 = TR0
      OUTPUT 2 = LP0
      END


      MASTER REGX
C     GENERAL REGRESSION PROGRAM 6.7.66

      COMMON / / A(144),B(144),C(60),D(15),E(125),F(15),G(15),W(2000),
     1     X(15),Y(15),Z(15),V,M
1     CONTINUE

      READ (1,9) Z0
299   FORMAT (/13H DATA SET NO  ,F5·2)
      IF (Z0 + 1·0) 13,0,13
C     PAUSE IF Z0 = −1
      PAUSE 1
      GO TO 1
289   FORMAT (100I0)

13    READ (1,289) I,L,M
      WRITE (2,299) Z0
      IF (I) 0,5,5
C     3 IS ERROR EXIT FROM READING IN MAIN DATA
39    FORMAT (/18H FAULTY CODE DIGIT)

3     WRITE (2,39)
C     READ AND IGNORE REST OF FAULTY DATA UP TO −1
40    FORMAT (100E0)

      GO TO 42

C     TEST THAT L AND M ARE POSITIVE
5     IF (L) 3,3,0
```

96

```
            IF (M) 3,3,0
            IF (I – 1) 0,7,3
C           READ DATA PUNCHED IN ROWS L ITEMS PER ROW M ROWS
            DO 6 I = 1,M
            READ (1,40) (W(I*L + J – L),  J = 1, L)
6           CONTINUE
C           CHECK THAT NEXT ITEM READ IS –1
10          FORMAT (3E0,I0)
21          READ (1,9) A0
C           READ NO ITEMS UP TO –1 IF A0 = –1 SWITCH
            IF (A0 + 1·0) 3,20,3

C           READ DATA PUNCHED IN COLS
7           DO 8 J = 1,L
            READ (1,40) (W(I*L + J – L), I = 1,M)
8           CONTINUE
            GO TO 21
C           READ CONTROL TAPE STARTING WITH CODE NO.A0 IF A0 = –1,
      1          READ NEW DATA
20          READ (1, 9) A0

290         FORMAT ( / 12H CONTROL NO,F5·2)
            IF (A0 + 1·0) 0,11,0
            WRITE (2,290) A0

16          READ (1,10) A1,B1,C1,K
            GO TO 12
41          FORMAT ( / 14H NEW MAIN DATA)
11          WRITE (2,41)
            GO TO 1
C           READ AND IGNORE CONTROLS UP TO NEXT MAIN DATA
9           FORMAT (4E0)
42          READ (1,9) A0
            IF (A0 + 1·0) 0,11,0
49          READ (1,9) C0
            IF (C0 + 1·0) 49,42,49
C           READ AND IGNORE UP TO END OF ONE CONTROL ONLY
47          READ (1,9) C0
            IF (C0 + 1·0) 47,20,47
C           CHECK CONTROL DIGITS

12          IF (A1) 0,14,14
C           A1 = 0 NO ACTION, = 1 PRINT RESIDUES, = 2 EXPECTED VALUES,
      1        = 3 BOTH
45          FORMAT ( / 14H CONTROL FAULT)
15          WRITE (2,45)
            GO TO 47
14          IF (A1 – 3·0) 0,0,15
```

```
C        B1 = 0 NO ACTION, B1 = 1 REMOVE MEANS FROM THE DATA
         IF (B1) 15,0,0
         IF (B1 – 1·0) 0,0,15
C        C1  IS PERCENT LEVEL FOR SIGNIFICANT T RATIOS
         IF (C1) 15,0,0
         IF (C1 – 100·0) 0,0,15
C        THERE ARE K X'S IN THE EQUATION, INCLUDING THE CONSTANT
         IF (K) 15,0,0
         IF (K – 12) 0,0,15
         K1 = 4*K + 8
         READ (1,9) (C(I), I = 1,K1)
         DO 17 I = 1,K1

         IF (C(I)) 15,0,0
17       CONTINUE
C        CHECK NEXT ITEM READ IS –1
18       READ (1,9) D1
         IF (D1 + 1·0) 0,19,0
22       FORMAT ( / 29H NO –1 ON END OF CONTROL TAPE)
         WRITE (2,22)
         GO TO 47
C        CLEAR SUMMATION SEQUENCES TO ZEROS
19       DO 23 I = 1,144
         A(I) = 0
23       B(I) = 0
         DS = 0
         ES = 0
         MD = M
         KD = K
         DO 24 I = 1,15
         D(I) = 0
         X(I) = 0
         Z(I) = 0
24       Y(I) = 0
         V = 0
         IF (C1) 15,0,25
26       FORMAT ( / 20H TRANSFORMED DATA IS)
         WRITE (2,26)
C        FIRST DATA CYCLE
25       IF (B1) 15,29,0
C        REMOVE MEANS, BUILD MEANS IN X SEQ. X(1) HOLDS SUM OF
       1     WEIGHTS
C        FINAL DATA IS IN Z SEQ
         KD = K + 1
         DO 27 J = 1,M
         CALL DATA (L,J,K,MD)
         X(1) = X(1) + Z(2)
         K1 = K + 2
```

98

```
          DO 27 I = 2,K1
27        X(I) = X(I) + Z(I + 1)*Z(2)
          X0 = 1·0/X(1)
          DO 28 I = 2,K1
28        X(I) = X(I)*X0
C         SECOND DATA CYCLE
43        FORMAT (5F14·5)
29        DO 32 J = 1,M
          CALL DATA (L,J,K,MD)
          DS = DS + Z(2)*Z(3)
          ES = ES + Z(2)*Z(3)*Z(3)
C         SUBTRACT MEANS OR ZEROS
          K2 = K + 2
          DO 95 I = 2,K2
95        Z(I + 1) = Z(I + 1) − X(I)
          IF (C1) 35, 0,35
          IF (J − 1) 0,0,37
          IF (V) 35,0,35
37        WRITE (2,43) (Z(I + 1),  I = 2,K2)
35        CONTINUE
C         SKIP FIRST TIME ROUND FOR DIFFERENCES
          IF (J − 1) 0,0,33
          IF (V) 32,0,32
C         V IS SWITCH DIGIT IN DIFFS SEQ
          INTEGER S,T
C         BUILD MATRIX XX
33        DO 30 T = 1,K
          DO 30 S = 1,K
30        A(K*T + S − K) = A(K*T + S − K) + Z(S + 3)*Z(T + 3)*Z(2)
C         BUILD VECTOR XY
          Y(3) = Y(3) + Z(2)
          Y(4) = Y(4) + Z(2)*Z(3)
          K1 = K + 1
          DO 31 I = 1,K1
31        Y(I + 4) = Y(I + 4) + Z(2)*Z(3)*Z(I + 2)
32        CONTINUE
          IF (C1) 36,0,36
34        FORMAT ( / 6H XX = )
          WRITE (2,34)
          DO 38 I = 1,K
          WRITE (2,43) (A(I*K + J − K), J = 1,I)
38        CONTINUE

C         INVERT XX MATRIX
36        CALL INVERT (K)
C         PRINT STATISTICS
          IF (K) 0,20,0
50        FORMAT ( / 5H B = , 6(F12·5))
```

```
C         PRINT B VECTOR
          DO 54 T = 1,K
          A(T + 2) = 0
          DO 55 S = 1,K
55        A(T + 2) = A(T + 2) + B(K*T + S − K)*Y(S + 5)
54        CONTINUE
          WRITE (2,50) (A(T + 2),  T = 1,K)
C         FORM BXY IN A(2)
          A(2) = 0
          DO 57 S = 1,K
57        A(2) = A(2) + A(S + 2)*Y(S + 5)
58        FORMAT ( / 5H C = ,F14·5,8H S SQ = ,F14·5,
     1            9H R1 SQ = ,F14·5,9H R2 SQ = ,F14·5)

          E1 = X(2)
          DO 59 I = 1,K
59        E1 = E1 − A(I + 2)*X(I + 2)
          F1 = 0
          IF (MD − KD) 0,51,0
          F1 = (Y(5) − A(2)) / (MD − KD)
51        G1 = 0
          IF (Y(5)) 0,53,0
          G1 = A(2) / Y(5)

53        H = 0
          IF (Y(3)) 0,52,0
          H = (((Y(4)*Y(4)) / Y(3)) − Y(5))
          H1 = ABS(H) − 1E − 8
          IF (H1) 52,52,0
          H = 1·0 + ((Y(5) − A(2)) / H)
52        CONTINUE
          WRITE (2,58) E1,F1,G1,H
          IF (H1) 20,20,0
C         MULTIPLY INVERSE BY S SQ
          DO 60 T = 1,K

          DO 60 S = 1,K
60        B(K*T + S − K) = B(K*T + S − K)*F1
C         TEST SIGNIFICANCE
61        FORMAT ( / 23H SE(B) =          T =        )

          WRITE (2,61)
C         PRINT STANDARD ERRORS AND T RATIOS
          DO 62 I = 1,K
          U = SQRT(ABS(B(I*K + I − K)))
          A(K + I + 2) = 0
          IF (U) 0,162,0
          A(K + I + 2) = A(I + 2) / U
```

100

```
162       CONTINUE
62        WRITE (2,43) U,A(K+I+2)
C         TEST FOR SIG T RATIO
          W0 = 0
          DO 63 I = 1,K
          IF (C1 - ABS(A(K+I+2))) 0,63,63
          W0 = W0 + 1·0
63        CONTINUE
74        IF (W0) 0,64,0

C         EXTRA PRINT IF ANY T IS SIGNIFICANT
69        FORMAT (5H M = ,I3,5H K = ,I3, 10H SUM W = ,F14·5,
     1        11H SUM WY = ,F14·5,12H SUM WYY = ,F14·5 / 6H XY = ,
     1    5(F14·5))

          WRITE (2,69) M,KD,Y(3),DS,ES, (Y(I+5),  I = 1,K)

72        FORMAT (9H V(B) =   )
          WRITE (2,72)
          DO 73 T = 1,K
          WRITE (2,43) (B(K*T+S-K),  S = 1,T)
73        CONTINUE

C         FORM RESIDUES
64        IF (A1) 0,20,0
C         PRINT RESIDUES AND/OR EXPECTED VALUES
78        FORMAT (/30H RESIDUES AND EXPECTED VALUES.)
          W0 = 0
          X0 = 0

          IF (A1 - 3·0) 93,0,0
          WRITE (2,78)

          GO TO 94
93        CONTINUE
          IF (A1 - 2·0) 0,97,0
          WRITE (2,98)
          GO TO 94
98        FORMAT (/10H RESIDUES.)
99        FORMAT (/17H EXPECTED VALUES.)
97        CONTINUE
          WRITE (2,99)
94        DO 84 J = 1,M
          CALL DATA (L,J,K,MD)
          IF (J-1) 0,0,79
          IF (V) 84, 0,84
79        Y0 = E1
          DO 81 I = 1,K
```

```
81      Y0 = Y0 + Z(I+3)*A(I+2)
        Z0 = Z(3) - Y0
        IF (A1 - 3·0) 88,0,0
        WRITE (2,43) Z0,Y0
        GO TO 83
88      IF (A1 - 2·0) 0,82,0
        WRITE (2,43) Z0
        GO TO 83

82      WRITE (2,43) Y0
83      IF (J - 1) 0,0,85
        D1 = Z0
85      X0 = X0 + (Z0 - D1)*(Z0 - D1)
        W0 = W0 + Z0*Z0
        D1 = Z0
84      CONTINUE
86      FORMAT (/12H SUM DESQ = ,F14·5,10H  SUM ESQ = ,F14·5,
     1          5HDW = ,F14·5/12H END OF REG.///)
C       PRINT DURBIN WATSON TESTS
        Y0 = 0
        IF (W0) 0,87,0
        Y0 = X0/W0
87      WRITE (2,86) X0,W0,Y0
75      GO TO 20
        END
        SUBROUTINE INVERT(K)
C       INVERSION OF MATRIX SUBROUTINE
        COMMON//A(144), B(144), C(60), D(15), E(125), F(15), G(15),
     1      W(2000), X(15), Y(15), Z(15), V, M
        INTEGER S,T
        K2 = K*K
        IF (K - 1) 0,116,0
        DO 102 I = 1,K2
102     B(I) = 0
        K1 = K + 1
        DO 103 I = 1,K2,K1
103     B(I) = 1·0
C       SEEK LARGEST ELEMENT
        DO 104 J = 1,K
        I = J
        X1 = 0

        DO 105 S = J,K
        Z1 = ABS(A(S*K + J - K))
        IF (X1 - Z1) 0,105,105
        X1 = Z1
        I = S
```

```
105      CONTINUE
         IF (I − J) 0,106,0
         DO 107 T = 1,K
         Z2 = A(K*J + T − K)
         A(K*J + T − K) = A(K*I + T − K)
         A(K*I + T − K) = Z2
         Y2 = B(K*J + T − K)
         B(K*J + T − K) = B(K*I + T − K)
107      B(K*I + T − K) = Y2
106      Y3 = ABS(A(K*J + J − K)) − 1E − 7
         IF (Y3) 0,0,108
         A(K*J + J − K) = 1E − 8
109      FORMAT (10H PIVOT = 0,2I4)
         WRITE (2,109) I,J

         K = 0
         GO TO 120

108      J1 = J + 1
         A3 = 1·0 / A(K*J + J − K)
         DO 110 T = J1,K
110      A(K*J + T − K) = A(K*J + T − K)*A3
         DO 111 T = 1,K
111      B(K*J + T − K) = B(K*J + T − K)*A3
         A(K*J + J − K) = 1·0
         DO 112 S = J1,K
         DO 113 T = J1,K
113      A(S*K + T − K) = A(K*S + T − K) − A(K*S + J − K)*A(K*J + T − K)
         DO 114 T = 1,K
114      B(K*S + T − K) = B(K*S + T − K) − A(K*S + J − K)*B(K*J + T − K)
112      A(K*S + J − K) = 0
104      CONTINUE
C        BACK SUBSTITUTE
         DO 115 K4 = 2,K
         T = K − K4 + 2
         DO 115 K5 = 2,T
         S = T − K5 + 1
         DO 115 J = 1,K
115      B(K*S + J − K) = B(S*K + J − K) − A(S*K + T − K)*B(K*T + J − K)
120      CONTINUE
         RETURN

116      IF (A(1)) 0,109,0
         B(1) = 1·0 / A(1)
         GO TO 120
         END

         SUBROUTINE DATA (L,J,K,MD)
```

```
C         BUILD DATA SUBROUTINE
          COMMON // A(144), B(144), C(60), D(15), E(125), F(15), G(15), W(2000),
     1    X(15), Y(15), Z(15), V, M
          INTEGER P,Q,R
          Z(1) = 1·0
          DO 201 R = 1,L
201       E(R) = W(L*J + R − L)
          K1 = K + 2
          DO 202 I = 1,K1
          P = INT(C(4*I − 2))
          IF (P) 90,0,90
          P = 1
90        E0 = E(P)
          P = INT(C(4*I − 3))
          IF (P) 91,0,91
          P = 1
91        F0 = E(P)
          Q = INT(C(4*I − 1)) + 1
          CALL DA2(Z0,I,J,Q,E0,F0,MD,L)
          Q = INT(C(4*I)) + 1
          F0 = Z0
          CALL DA2(Z0,I,J,Q,E0,F0,MD,L)
202       Z(I + 1) = Z0
          RETURN
          END


          SUBROUTINE DA2(Z0,I,J,Q,E0,F0,MD,L)
          COMMON // A(144), B(144), C(60), D(15), E(125), F(15), G(15), W(2000),
     1    X(15), Y(15), Z(15), V, M
          INTEGER Q
          GO TO (210, 211, 212, 213, 214, 215, 216, 217, 218, 219, 220, 221, 222,
     1    223), Q
203       CONTINUE
          RETURN
210       Z0 = F0
          GO TO 203
211       Z0 = E0 + F0
          GO TO 203
212       Z0 = F0 − E0
          GO TO 203
213       Z0 = E0*F0
          GO TO 203
214       IF (E0) 0,234,0
          Z0 = F0/E0
          GO TO 203
233       FORMAT (13H ZERO DIVISOR)
234       WRITE (2,233)
          Z0 = 1E8
```

104

```
        GO TO 203
215     IF (F0) 238,238,0
236     Z0 = ALOG(F0)
        GO TO 203
216     Z0 = EXP(F0)
        GO TO 203
217     Z0 = F0*F0
        GO TO 203
218     IF (F0) 0,234, 0
        Z0 = 1·0/F0
        GO TO 203
219     IF (F0) 0,0,237
232     FORMAT (13H NEGATIVE LOG)
238     WRITE (2,232)
        GO TO 203
237     Z0 = ALOG(F0)*ALOG(F0)
        GO TO 203
220     D(I) = Z(I+1) + D(I)
        Z0 = F0 - D(I)
        IF (J - 1) 0,0,203
        IF (V) 0, 0,225
        V = V + 1·0

        MD = M - 1
225     Z(2) = 0
235     GO TO 203
222     IF (E0) 0,234,0
        IF (F0) 0,234,0
        Z0 = 1·0/(E0*F0)
        GO TO 203
221     Z0 = 1·0
        GO TO 203
223     Z0 = L
        GO TO 203


        END
        FINISH
```

§2.14 Sample of input to REGX

```
99

0    5    13

7    26    6    60    78·5
1    29    15    52    74·3
11    56    8    20    104·3
```

Main data punched in rows, 13 rows of 5 observations per row, that is 5 variables and 13 observations on each variable.

11	31	8	47	87·6
7	52	6	33	95·9
11	55	9	22	109·2
3	71	17	6	102·7
1	31	22	44	72·5
2	54	18	22	93·1
21	47	4	26	115·9
1	40	23	34	83·8
11	66	9	12	113·3
10	68	8	12	109·4

−1

99

2	0	0	0	The regression equation is
0	0	11	0	
5	0	0	0	
0	0	11	0	
1	0	0	0	
2	0	0	0	
3	0	0	0	
4	0	0	0	

The regression equation is

$$y = c + b_1 x_1 + b_2 x_2 + b_3 x_3 + b_4 x_4$$

Full print with expected values.
The weight $w = 1$.

y is column 5 in the data.

$x_0 = 1$

x_1 is column 1 in the data.

x_2 is column 2

x_3 is column 3

x_4 is column 4.

−1

−1

§2.15 Output of test data from REGX

DATA SET NO   99·00

CONTROL NO   99·00

TRANSFORMED DATA IS

78·50000	1·00000	7·00000	26·00000
6·00000	60·00000		
74·30000	1·00000	1·000000	29·00000
15·00000	52·00000		
104·30000	1·00000	11·00000	56·00000
8·00000	20·00000		

87·60000	1·00000	11·00000	31·00000
8·00000	47·00000		
95·90000	1·00000	7·00000	52·00000
6·00000	33·00000		
109·20000	1·00000	11·00000	55·00000
9·00000	22·00000		
102·70000	1·00000	3·00000	71·00000
17·00000	6·00000		
72·50000	1·00000	1·00000	31·00000
22·00000	44·00000		
93·10000	1·00000	2·00000	54·00000
18·00000	22·00000		
115·90000	1·00000	21·00000	47·00000
4·00000	26·00000		
83·80000	1·00000	1·00000	40·00000
23·00000	34·00000		
113·30000	1·00000	11·00000	66·00000
9·00000	12·00000		
109·40000	1·00000	10·00000	68·00000
8·00000	12·00000		

XX =

13·00000				
97·00000	1139·00000			
626·00000	4922·00000	33050·00000		
153·00000	769·00000	7201·00000	2293·00000	
390·00000	2620·00000	15739·00000	4628·00000	
15062·00000				

B =

62·40501	1·55110	0·51017	0·10191
−0·14406			

C = 0·00000 $S\ SQ$ = 5·98678 $R1\ SQ$ = 0·99960 $R2\ SQ$ = 0·98236

$SE(B)$ =	70·00000	T =	0·89032
	0·74501		2·08201
	0·72402		0·70463
	0·75495		0·13499
	0·70928		−0·20311

M = 13 K = 5   SUM W = 13·00000   SUM WY = 1240·500000

SUM WYY = 121090·00000

XY = 1240·50000   10032·00000   62028·00000   13982·00000   34733·00000

$V(B)$ =

4913·10020			
−50·53901	0·55504		
−50·63450	0·51298	0·52420	
−51·69301	0·55460	0·52604	0·56995
−49·62902	0·50561	0·51246	0·51721
0·50308			

EXPECTED VALUES

$$
\begin{array}{r}
78 \cdot 49501 \\
72 \cdot 78902 \\
105 \cdot 96667 \\
89 \cdot 32689 \\
95 \cdot 64889 \\
105 \cdot 26897 \\
104 \cdot 14455 \\
75 \cdot 67500 \\
91 \cdot 72201 \\
115 \cdot 62030 \\
81 \cdot 80901 \\
112 \cdot 33303 \\
111 \cdot 68976
\end{array}
$$

SUM *DE SQ* = 98·24501   SUM *E SQ* = 47·86402   *DW* = 2·05256

END OF REG

Further reading on elementary statistics and regression analysis will be found in:

> Brookes and Dick (1951),
> Cramer (1945),
> Croxton and Cowden (1955),
> Ezekiel (1941),
> Fisher (1950),
> Kendall (1943, 1946),
> Loveday (1960, 1961)

and Weatherburn (1947).

3   LINEAR PROGRAMMING

SECTION 1

THE ELEMENTS OF THE SIMPLEX PROCESS

§3.1 Introduction

The concept of linear programming arises naturally as an extension of multiple linear regression analysis. In general regression analysis we have a specialised function

$$Q \; = \; \sum_{i=1}^{M} \left(Y_i - a - \sum_{v=1}^{N} b_v \, X_{iv} \right)^2 \tag{3.1.1}$$

of the dependent variables

$$X_{i1}, \; X_{i2}, \; X_{i3}, \; \ldots \quad \ldots, \; X_{iN}$$

and the independent variable Y_i, and we wish to minimise this function Q, that is to find those values of $a, b_1, b_2, b_3, \ldots \ldots, b_N$, for which Q assumes its least possible numerical value. Since Q is a sum of squares, its value is always positive.

If we substitute the general linear function

$$c \; = \; c_1 b_1 \; + \; c_2 b_2 \; + \; c_3 b_3 \; + \; \ldots \quad \ldots \; + \; c_n b_n, \tag{3.1.2}$$

for our special function Q, and write x_v for b_v, we can consider the general problem of minimising the numerical value of

$$c \; = \; c_1 x_1 \; + \; c_2 x_2 \; + \; c_3 x_3 \; + \; \ldots \quad \ldots \; + \; c_n x_n, \tag{3.1.3}$$

subject to constraints on the variables

$$x_1, x_2, x_3, \ldots \quad \ldots, x_n.$$

We note that there is no problem to be solved if any x can be unbounded below, and negative, since then c can become infinitely large and negative. Hence we have to assume that all the x's are bounded below, or, which is equivalent in this context, that all the x's are positive or zero.

Further, to take the place of the normal equations, we assume the existence of a set of m constraints among the n x's of the form

$$
\begin{aligned}
a_{11} x_1 + a_{12} x_2 + a_{13} x_3 + \ldots \quad \ldots + a_{1n} x_n &= b_1, \\
a_{21} x_1 + a_{22} x_2 + a_{23} x_3 + \ldots \quad \ldots + a_{2n} x_n &= b_2, \\
a_{31} x_1 + a_{32} x_2 + a_{33} x_3 + \ldots \quad \ldots + a_{3n} x_n &= b_3, \\
\ldots\ldots \qquad\qquad \ldots\ldots \\
a_{m1} x_1 + a_{m2} x_2 + a_{m3} x_3 + \ldots \quad \ldots + a_{mn} x_n &= b_m.
\end{aligned}
\tag{3.1.4}
$$

These m equations are assumed to be linearly independent, that is, no set of coefficients is a constant multiple of any other set. Otherwise one or more of the equations could be dropped, and the value of m decreased in order to reduce the set to a truly linearly independent form. So, given the values of $a_{11}, a_{12}, a_{13}, \ldots \ldots, a_{mn}, b_1, b_2, b_3, \ldots, b_m,$ and $c_1, c_2, c_3, \ldots, c_n,$ the problem is then simply to find non-negative values of $x_1, x_2, x_3, \ldots, x_n,$ which make c a minimum, and which satisfy all the constraints at once.

Problems of this type arise frequently throughout economics. Though it is possible in very simple cases to carry through the calculations by the use of hand calculating machines, usually the number of variables and the number of equations involved is so great that the use of an electronic computer becomes imperative.

In multiple regression analysis, we arrive at a formal solution by forming various partial derivatives and equating these to zero, in order to find the minimum, that is the lowest point on the surface, from a geometrical point of view. In the present problem, such methods are not helpful, as the minimum point which we seek nearly always falls on the boundary of the region which we are considering, and, at such a point, some or all of the derivatives are not defined at all. However, there are still many possible ways of finding a solution. In the present elementary discussion, we shall first try to find any non-negative set of x's which satisfies the equations, and then we shall try to adjust these values in some systematic way, to find the minimum value of c. This is the basis of the original simplex methods, developed by Dantzig (1955).

§3.2 An elementary example

Let us consider a very simple example, in order to clarify these ideas. Suppose that we are given three equations

$$x_1 + 2x_2 + 3x_3 = 4,$$
$$2x_1 + 3x_2 + 4x_4 = 10, \qquad (3.2.1)$$
$$x_1 + x_2 + x_3 + x_5 = 6,$$

and we wish to find the minimum value assumed by

$$A = x_3 - x_2,$$

under the condition that all the x's are positive or zero. First we have to find any solution of these three equations which makes two of the five variables zero and all the other variables positive. Such a solution is called a basic feasible solution. If we assume that x_1 and x_2 are zero, then one such solution of these three equations is

$$x_1 = 0, \quad x_2 = 0, \quad x_3 = 4/3, \quad x_4 = 5/2, \quad x_5 = 14/3. \qquad (3.2.2)$$

Now we have to express the three non-zero variables $x_3, x_4,$ and x_5 and the functional A in terms of the two zero variables x_1 and x_2, so that

$$x_3 = \frac{4}{3} - \frac{x_1}{3} - \frac{2x_2}{3},$$

$$x_4 = \frac{10}{4} - \frac{2x_1}{4} - \frac{3x_2}{4},$$

and

$$x_5 = 6 - x_1 - x_2 - \frac{4}{3} + \frac{1}{3}x_1 + \frac{2}{3}x_2,$$

that is

$$x_5 = \frac{14}{3} - \frac{2}{3}x_1 - \frac{1}{3}x_2,$$

and

$$A = \frac{4}{3} - \frac{1}{3}x_1 - \frac{5}{3}x_2. \tag{3.2.3}$$

Here we have A expressed in terms of x_1 and x_2 only. Next we select that variable from those which occur in the expression for A, which has the greatest coefficient. In this case it is x_2. Obviously any increase in x_2 will decrease the value of A, but increasing x_2 decreases x_3, and x_4 and x_5 also. So we see that x_2 can only be increased until x_3, x_4 or x_5 becomes zero, as all the x's are constrained to be positive or zero. Since of these three variables x_4 contains the largest coefficient of $x_2, -\frac{3}{4}$, we now make x_4 equal to zero. Then we find that $x_2 = \frac{10}{3}$ and $x_1 = 0$. But this violates the condition $x_3 \geqslant 0$.

Next we have to re-express our three equations and A in terms of our new zero variables x_1 and x_4.
That is

$$x_2 = \frac{-2}{3}x_1 - \frac{4}{3}x_4 + \frac{10}{3},$$

$$x_3 = \frac{1}{9}x_1 + \frac{8}{9}x_4 - \frac{8}{9},$$

and

$$x_5 = \frac{14}{3} - \frac{2}{3}x_1 + \frac{1}{3}\left(\frac{2}{3}x_1\right) + \frac{1}{3}\left(\frac{4}{3}x_4\right) - \frac{1}{3}\left(\frac{10}{3}\right),$$

that is

$$x_5 = -\frac{4}{9}x_1 + \frac{4}{9}x_4 + \frac{32}{9}.$$

Also

$$A = -\frac{1}{3}x_1 + \frac{5}{3}\left(\frac{2}{3}x_1\right) + \frac{5}{3}\left(\frac{4}{3}x_4\right) - \frac{5}{3}\left(\frac{10}{3}\right) + \frac{4}{3},$$

that is

$$A = \frac{7}{9}x_1 + \frac{20}{9}x_4 - \frac{38}{9}. \tag{3.2.4}$$

Here A is expressed now in terms of x_1 and x_4 only.

Next we select x_4, as that variable from those that occur in A, which has the greatest coefficient, and we increase x_4 until x_3 becomes zero. Then $x_4 = 4$. We can re-express all the equations in the terms of x_1 and x_3 and we find that

$$x_4 = -\frac{1}{8}x_1 + \frac{9}{8}x_3 + 1,$$

111

$$x_2 = -\frac{2}{3}x_1 - \frac{4}{3}\left(-\frac{1}{8}x_1 + \frac{9}{8}x_3 + 1\right) + \frac{10}{3},$$

that is
$$x_2 = -\frac{1}{2}x_1 - \frac{3}{2}x_3 + 2,$$

and
$$x_5 = -\frac{4}{9}x_1 + \frac{4}{9}\left(-\frac{1}{8}x_1 + \frac{9}{8}x_3 + 1\right) + \frac{32}{9},$$

that is
$$x_5 = -\frac{1}{2}x_1 + \frac{1}{2}x_3 + 4,$$

and
$$A = \frac{7}{9}x_1 + \frac{20}{9}\left(-\frac{1}{8}x_1 + \frac{9}{8}x_3 + 1\right) - \frac{38}{9},$$

that is
$$A = \frac{1}{2}x_1 + \frac{5}{2}x_3 - 2. \tag{3.2.5}$$

Here A is expressed in terms of x_1 and x_3 only.

Any increase in x_1 or in x_3 will now result only in an increase in the value of A. Hence the required minimal solution in A has been found, and A has its minimum value -2, at the point

$$x_1 = 0, \quad x_2 = 2, \quad x_3 = 0, \quad x_4 = 1, \quad x_5 = 4.$$

A more efficient layout for hand computation is achieved by treating the coefficients as a matrix, and then the x's in the equation need not be written down at all. The above example would then become

c	x_1	x_2	x_3	x_4	x_5	A
-4	1	2	3	0	0	0
-10	2	3	0	4	0	0
-6	1	1	1	0	1	0
0	0	-1	1	0	0	1

One solution which makes all the x's positive or zero has $x_1 = 0$, and $x_2 = 0$, so that we can express everything in terms of x_1 and x_2.

	c	x_1	x_2				
x_3	$\frac{4}{3}$	$-\frac{1}{3}$	$-\frac{2}{3}$	1	0	0	0
x_4	$\frac{5}{2}$	$-\frac{1}{2}$	$-\frac{3}{4}$	0	1	0	0
x_5	$\frac{14}{3}$	$-\frac{2}{3}$	$-\frac{1}{3}$	0	0	1	0
A	$\frac{4}{3}$	$-\frac{1}{3}$	$-\frac{5}{3}$	0	0	0	1

We note that the last four columns form a unit matrix, with 1's down the diagonal and 0's everywhere else, so that we do not need to write out these last four columns every time. We select that variable from x_1 and x_2 which has the greatest coefficient in A, that is x_2. We select next that variable from x_3, x_4 and x_5, with the largest coefficient in x_2, that is x_4. Now we re-express everything in terms of the new zero variables x_1 and x_4.

	c	x_1	x_4
x_2	$\dfrac{10}{3}$	$-\dfrac{2}{3}$	$-\dfrac{4}{3}$
x_3	$-\dfrac{8}{9}$	$\dfrac{1}{9}$	$\dfrac{8}{9}$
x_5	$\dfrac{32}{9}$	$-\dfrac{4}{9}$	$\dfrac{4}{9}$
A	$-\dfrac{38}{9}$	$\dfrac{7}{9}$	$\dfrac{20}{9}$

Then we select from x_1 and x_4 that variable with the greatest coefficient in A, that is x_4, and select from x_2, x_3, or x_5, that variable with the greatest coefficient in x_4, that is x_3, so that we can express everything in terms of x_1 and x_3, starting this time with the row for x_4. We find:—

	c	x_1	x_3
x_2	2	$-\dfrac{1}{2}$	$-\dfrac{3}{2}$
x_4	1	$-\dfrac{1}{8}$	$\dfrac{9}{8}$
x_5	4	$-\dfrac{1}{2}$	$\dfrac{1}{2}$
A	-2	$\dfrac{1}{2}$	$\dfrac{5}{2}$

Hence A has its minimum at -2, as before, and the complete solution is contained in the first column of our array.

§3.3 Linear programming on an electronic computer

This is about as far as we can go, using hand-calculating machines. Although the actual calculations are very simple, the size of the matrix involved in practical problems is usually very large, and the number of steps required to reach a solution also becomes very large, so that we are forced to consider the organization of our calculations for automatic computing methods. The main method outlined above, the simplex method was first programmed for an electronic computer in 1950 at Manchester by D.G. Prinz.

The first step is to restate the problem in such a way that it can be expressed in exact numerical terms. Suppose that we are given the example:—

If

$$x_2 - 2x_1 \leqslant 1,$$
$$-x_1 - 2x_2 \leqslant 2, \tag{3.3.1}$$
$$x_1 + x_2 \leqslant 3,$$

and x_1 and x_2 are $\geqslant 0$, find the *least numerical value of*

$$C = x_2 - x_1. \qquad (3.3.2)$$

First we introduce the so-called "slack variables" x_3, x_4 and x_5, and we re-express the problem to get rid of the inequality signs. The example becomes:—

Minimize $\qquad C = -x_1 + x_2,$ $\qquad\qquad\qquad\qquad\qquad$ (3.3.3)

given that $\qquad\ 1 = -2x_1 + x_2 + x_3$

$\qquad\qquad\qquad\quad 2 = -x_1 - 2x_2 \qquad\ + x_4,$ $\qquad\qquad\qquad$ (3.3.4)

$\qquad\qquad\qquad\quad 3 = \ \ x_1 + x_2 \qquad\qquad\ + x_5,$

and all x's $\geqslant 0$.

In algebraic terms the general form is:—

Minimize

$$C = \sum_{v=1}^{n} c_v x_v, \qquad (3.3.5)$$

given that $\qquad\qquad b_u = \sum_{v=1}^{n} a_{uv} x_v, \text{ for } u = 0, 1, 2, \ldots, m-1,$

where all $x_v \geqslant 0$.

As in most practical problems, the total number of variables and of equations may be very large, it is important to consider carefully the form to be taken by the input data. Whilst this should contain everything necessary to the calculation, it should also contain nothing irrelevant. For our example the layout of the input data might be

3	5		−1	1	0	0	0	/
		1	−2	1	1	0	0	
		2	−1	−2	0	1	0	
		3	1	1	0	0	1	/,

where / is a terminating symbol to enable the computer to take note of the number of elements in the data sequence it has just read.

In general algebraic terms we would restate this as

$m,$	$n,$					
	$c_0,$	c_1	$c_2,$	$\ldots$ $\ldots$	$c_{n-1},$	/
$b_0,$	$a_{00},$	$a_{01},$	$a_{02},$	$\ldots$ $\ldots$	$a_{0,n-1},$	
$b_1,$	$a_{10},$	$a_{11},$	$a_{12},$	$\ldots$ $\ldots$	$a_{1,n-1},$	
$b_2,$	$a_{20},$	$a_{21},$	$a_{22},$	$\ldots$ $\ldots$	$a_{2,n-1},$	
$\ldots\ldots$					$\ldots\ldots$	
$b_{m-1},$	$a_{m-1,0},$	$a_{m-1,1},$	$a_{m-1,2},$	$\ldots$ $\ldots$	$a_{m-1,n-1}$	/.

Here there are n items in the first row, and m rows in the main matrix. In the example, $m = 3$ and $n = 5$. This first row will be called the R_0 row, and the other rows will be called rows $R_1, R_2, R_3, \ldots \ldots, R_m$. The computer first checks that in fact there are n items in the first row it has read and $m(n+1)-1$ items in the whole matrix. Three extra rows are set up by the computer, the row called R_{-1}, which consists of the sums of each column of the rows $R_1, R_2, R_3, ..., R_m$, (excluding the row R_0), the row called the "I" table, which contains the suffixes of the slack variables, (which are always m in number), and the row called the "J" table table, which contains the suffixes of all the other variables (which are always $m-n$ in number).

Thus for this example, we have to set up within the computer the matrix:—

I table

6	− 2	0	1	1	1		R_{-1} row
0	− 1	1	0	0	0		R_0 row
1	− 2	1	1	0	0	3	R_1 row
2	− 1	− 2	0	1	0	4	R_2 row
3	1	1	0	0	1	5	R_3 row
	1	2					J table

We shall refer to the elements of the row R_0 as

$$C, c_0, c_1, c_2, ... \quad ... c_{n-1},$$

and the elements of the row R_{-1} as

$$V, v_0, v_1, v_2, ... \quad ..., v_{n-1}.$$

Also we shall say that those x's whose suffixes appear in the I table, initially the slack variables, are "within the basis" for the current iteration, and those x's whose suffixes appear in the J table, are "outside the basis" for the current iteration. The whole simplex process comes down to the problem of selecting an x from those listed in the I table to be removed from the current basis, and another x from those listed in the J table to replace it in the current basis.

The process has three stages. The first stage is to select which is the best x to be brought into the basis, the second stage is to decide which is the best x to be removed from the basis, and the third stage is to transform the matrix itself.

Stage 1. The initial basic feasible solution in our example contains x_3, x_4, and x_5, and the columns representing these variables in our matrix have 1's in the R_{-1} row. We use this row to make our first test, and we select from row R_{-1} that element v_k which has the greatest negative value. Then the kth number in the J table gives us the suffix k of the variable x_k which is the x to be brought into the basis.

If all the elements of row R_{-1} had been $\geqslant 0$, then we could have carried out a further test on the elements

$$c_0, c_1, c_2, ... \quad ..., c_{n-1}$$

of row R_0 and selected that column of those with a zero v_j which had the greatest negative c_j. If in fact there was no such negative c_j present in row R_0, then we could conclude that our process was finished, and that no further cycles could improve the value of C.

Stage 2. Just as we have called our rows $R_0, R_1, ..., R_m$, in our matrix, so also we shall call the columns of our matrix $C_1, C_2, C_3, ...$ ..., C_n, and the first column, which contains the b's, C_0. In order to decide which x has to be removed from the basis, we form a new column, outside our matrix (which we shall call the C_{-1} column), by dividing each element of column C_0 by the corresponding element of column C_k, which in this example we see is in fact column C_1.

	C_{-1}	C_0	C_1	C_2	C_3	C_4	C_5	I
R_{-1}		6	-2	0	1	1	1	
R_0		0	-1	1	0	0	0	
R_1	$-\frac{1}{2}$	1	-2	1	1	0	0	3
R_2	-2	2	-1	-2	0	1	0	4
R_3	3	3	(1)	1	0	0	1	5
J			1	2				

We now select the least positive element t_p from the column C_{-1}. Then the p'th number in the I table gives us the suffix r of x_r the variable which is to be forced out of the current basis. In this case it is x_5.

Stage 3. We now transform the whole matrix by introducing column C_p into the basis and dropping column C_k out of the basis. First we select the ringed element x_{pk} as our pivot. Here $p = 3$, $k = 1$ and $x_{31} = 1$. We form a new pivot row R'_p by the rule

$$R'_p = \frac{1}{x_{pk}} R_p, \tag{3.3.6}$$

and new rows for the rest of our matrix, including rows R_{-1} and R_0, according to the rule

$$R'_s = R_s - x_{sk} R'_p, \tag{3.3.7}$$

that is to say, we first divide every element in the pivot row by the pivot itself, and then form new elements for the rest of the matrix by subtracting from the existing element the product of the corresponding element in the new pivot row, and the element in the pivot column. We also interchange the suffixes in the I and J tables, replacing r by k in the I table and k by r in the J table. Our matrix is now

$$6-(-2)3/1, -2-(-2)1/1, \quad 0-(-2)1/1, 1-(-2)0/1, 1-(-2)0/1, 1-(-2)1/1,$$
$$0-(-1)3/1, -1-(-1)1/1, \quad 1-(-1)1/1, 0-(-1)0/1, 0-(-1)0/1, 0-(-1)1/1,$$
$$-\tfrac{1}{2}, \quad 1-(-2)3/1, -2-(-2)1/1, \quad 1-(-2)1/1, 1-(-2)0/1, 0-(-2)0/1, 0-(-2)1/1, 3$$
$$-2, \quad 2-(-1)3/1, -1-(-1)1/1, -2-(-1)1/1, 0-(-1)0/1, 1-(-1)0/1, 0-(-1)1/1, 4$$
$$3, \quad 3/1, \quad 1/1, \quad 1/1, \quad 0/1, \quad 0/1, \quad 1/1, \quad 1$$
$$5 \qquad 2$$

that is to say,

	C_{-1}	C_0						I
R_{-1}		12	0	2	1	1	3	
R_0		3	0	2	0	0	1	
	$-\frac{1}{2}$	7	0	3	1	0	2	3
	-2	5	0	-1	0	1	1	4
	3	3	1	1	0	0	1	1
J		5	2					

Now we return to stage 1 and try to repeat the cycle. We look along our first row R_{-1} and find that it now has no negative elements. So we look along those elements of the second row R_0 which occur against zero elements in the first row. There is only one of these in column one, and as this element is not negative but zero we conclude that the process is finished.

The actual answers are contained in the C_0 column of our matrix, and this should now be printed together with the numbers in the I table to tell us which variables remain in the final basis, and the order in which their values are printed. In our example, the numbers printed would be

$$-C = 3, \quad I = 3, \quad x = 7{\cdot}0, \quad I = 4, \quad x = 5{\cdot}0, \quad I = 1, \quad x = 3{\cdot}0, \quad J = 5{\cdot}2.$$

This output tells us that the complete answer is $-C = 3$, when $x_1 = 3$, $x_2 = 0$, $x_3 = 7$, $x_4 = 5$ and $x_5 = 0$, that is to say that C has its minimum value -3 at $(3, 0, 7, 5, 0)$. The change in the sign of C should be noted.

§3.4 The contracted simplex process

There are three main shortcomings in the ordinary simplex process outlined above, which we discover only after we have tried a few practical problems for ourselves, by using an actual electronic computer. The first of these is the problem of storage space for our matrix. The actual matrices used in practical economic problems are usually very large, up to about 150×100 elements or even larger, and the biggest computer usually cannot hold such a matrix in its main storage. We are forced then to store the matrix on magnetic tape or on some other form of auxiliary storage.

We then run into our second problem, which is that the time taken to work out a complete solution becomes very long. As the number of variables in our matrix increases, so does the number of cycles required to reach the minimum value. It can be proved that the minimum is always able to be reached in a finite number of cycles, but even if we are using a very fast computer, a large matrix might take several hours to process.

The third difficulty is a numerical one. It arises from the fact that we have to carry out a large number of cycles to process a big matrix. At every cycle we ought to form exact 0's and 1's in the columns representing our basis. In fact at each single stage a small error is made so that after a large number of cycles, the 0's and 1's cease to be exact, and the tests which we apply to the R_{-1} and the R_0 rows cease to work properly.

117

The contracted simplex process which we shall now outline relieves the first and second difficulties to some extent, by reducing the size of the actual matrix stored in the machine, and the trick known as "the cut off at the critical point" removes the third difficulty in most cases.

First we notice that the columns of our matrix which refer to x's in the current basis contain only 0's and 1's throughout, so that there is no need to store them explicitly within the store of our machine. Instead we can set up our initial matrix as

C_0	C_1	C_2			C_{n-m}		I
v_{-1}	v_0	v_1	$\cdots$	$\cdots$	v_{n-m-1}		R_{-1}
C	c_0	c_1	$\cdots$	$\cdots$	c_{n-m-1}		R_0
b_1	a_{10}	a_{11}	$\cdots$	$\cdots$	$a_{1,n-m-1}$	$N+1$	R_1
b_2	a_{20}	a_{21}	$\cdots$	$\cdots$	$a_{2,n-m-1}$	$N+2$	R_2
$\cdots$					$\cdots$		
b_m	$a_{m,0}$	$a_{m,1}$	$\cdots$	$\cdots$	$a_{m,n-m-1}$	$N+m$	R_m
0	1		$\cdots$	$\cdots$	$n-m-1$		J

where $C = 0$, initially, and the row R_{-1} consists of minus the sums of the columns of the matrix, excluding row R_0, that is to say

$$-v_{-1} = b_1 + b_2 + \ldots + b_m,$$
$$-v_0 = a_{10} + a_{20} + \ldots + a_{m,0},$$

$$\cdots\cdots\cdots$$

and so on. The J table is set up as

$0, 1, 2, \ldots, (n - m - 1), (n - m$ items), to represent the suffixes of those variables not in the initial basic solution, and the I table is set up as $N + 1, N + 2, \ldots, N + m, (m$ items), (where N is some fixed large positive integer) to represent the suffixes of those "slack" variables, which form the initial basis for a solution. Here the size of the main matrix is not $m \times n$ as it was previously, but only $m(n - m)$, which is much smaller.

Again the program has three sections.

(i) *The K section.* This section is to discover which variable x_k is the best one to introduce into the basis. The program first tests if the so-called "critical point" has been reached in the calculation, by testing all the numbers in the I table. If any of these is $> N$, the critical point has not been reached and the program goes on to do the rest of the tests in the K sequence calculations.

If however all the numbers in the I table are $\leqslant N$, every element of row, R_{-1} (which at this critical point now contains approximate 0's and 1's only) is replaced by an exact 1 if the corresponding J index is $> N$ and an exact 0 otherwise. This prevents the programme from getting into an infinite cycle at this point, due to the accumulated small errors. When once this point has been reached, this test can be ignored in future cycles.

The main part of the K section seeks along the rows R_{-1} and R_0 as before, to find the greatest negative v_j or, if all the v_j's are $\geqslant 0$, the great-

118

est negative c_j, from those columns which have $v_j = 0$. If all the v_j 's are $\geqslant 0$ and there is no negative c_j left, the process of minimizing is finished, and the program can go on to the final print sequences. If however, the greatest negative v_j (or c_j) occurs in column C_k, then K is the address of the suffix k in the J table of the best variable x_k to introduce into the basis.

(ii) *The R section.* This section discovers which variable x_r is the best to remove from the basis. It forms the m ratios t_u, by dividing the element in column C_0 by that in column C_k, that is

$$t_u = b_u / a_{uk}. \tag{3.4.1}$$

Then it seeks the least positive t_u, t_p, where p is the address in the I table of the suffix r of the best variable x_r to be removed from the basis.

(iii) *The X section.* This section transforms the entire matrix including column C_0 and rows R_0 and R_{-1}, by the rules

$$x'_{pk} = 1/x_{pk} \qquad \text{for the pivot element } x_{pk}, \tag{3.4.2}$$

$$x'_{ps} = x_{ps}/x_{pk}, \quad s \neq k, \quad \text{for the main row } R_p, \tag{3.4.3}$$

$$x'_{uk} = -x_{uk}/x_{pk}, u \neq p \quad \text{for the main column } C_k, \tag{3.4.4}$$

$$\text{and} \quad x'_{us} = x_{us} - x_{ps}x_{uk}/x'_{pk}, \, u \neq p \text{ and } s \neq k, \tag{3.4.5}$$

for all the rest of the matrix. Also k from the K'th place in the J table is exchanged with r from the p'th place in the I table. Then the program returns to the start of the K section to do another cycle.

The output produced by such a program should be kept to a minimum if the matrix is large. Usually it is enough to print the values of C, k and r at each cycle, to keep track of the progress of the calculation, and to print the row R_0, the column C_0 and the contents of the I and J tables at the finish of the calculation.

As an example, the problem is to minimize

$$C = -x_1 + x_2, \tag{3.4.6}$$

$$\text{given that} \qquad 2 \leqslant -2x_1 + x_2,$$

$$2 \leqslant x_1 - 2x_2 \tag{3.4.7}$$

$$\text{and} \qquad 5 \leqslant x_1 + x_2.$$

The input data is

3	2	
−1	1	
2	−2	1
2	1	−2
5	1	1 .

Here $m = 3$ and $n - m = 2$, so that actually $n = 5$. The initial basis of slack variables consists of the variables x_3, x_4 and x_5, so that we set up our tables as 103, 104, 105, for the I table, where we have taken $N = 100$, and 1, 2 for the J table, as the other variables are x_1 and x_2.

Cycle I. The initial table is:

C_0	C_1	C_2	C_{-1}	I	
9	0	0			R_{-1}
0	-1	1			R_0
2	-2	1	-1	103	R_1
2	1	-2	2	104	R_2
5	1	1	5	105	R_3
	1	2			J

Here minimum $v_j = 0$, minimum $c_j = -1$, so that x_1 must go into the basis. The least positive $t_u = 2$, so that x_4 goes out of the basis.

Cycle II. The transformed matrix is:

9	0	0		
2	1	-1		
6	2	-3	-2	103
2	1	-2	-1	1
3	-1	3	1	105
	104	2		

Here minimum $v_j = 0$, and minimum $c_j = -1$, so that x_2 goes into the basis, and the least positive t_u is 1, so that x_5 goes out of the basis.

Cycle III. The transformed matrix is now:

9	0	0		
3	2/3	1/3		
9	1	1	103	
4	1/3	2/3	1	
1	-1/3	1/3	2	
	104	105		

There is now no negative v_j or c_j left so that the process is finished and the final output is:

$$C = \quad -3 \quad\quad 2/3 \quad\quad 1/3 \quad\quad J = 4, 5$$
$$x = \quad\quad 9 \quad\quad 4 \quad\quad 1$$
$$I = \quad 103 \quad\quad 1 \quad\quad 2$$

This tells us that the minimum value of C is -3, when

$$C = -3 + \frac{2}{3}x_4 + \frac{1}{3}x_5,$$

and $x_1 = 4$, $x_2 = 1$, $x_3 = 9$, $x_4 = 0$, and $x_5 = 0$,

(see also Vadja (1956) p.36 for an alternative discussion).

120

§3.5 A practical example

In any linear programming problem, there are three stages that we have to carry out in order to produce meaningful results. The first stage consists of collecting our initial data and in setting up the system of equations which connect our variables. The second stage is the actual carrying out of the calculations, and the third stage is the interpreting of our results. In this present work, we are concerned mainly with the problem of doing the calculations accurately, but we give here an example to show all the three stages of a calculation.

Suppose that on a farm we are able to grow four crops, C, corn, O, oats, G, grass and W, wheat. We know N, the net profit made per acre for each crop. We know also M, the labour required for planting one acre in March, A, the labour required for harvesting one acre in August and L, the land available in acres for each crop.

This is our basic data, which we have obtained by observation and measurement. We must be very careful to express all these quantities accurately in their correct units.

Data table,	Corn	Oats	Grass	Wheat
N in £ per acre	30	10	40	12
M in man-days per acre	0	1	0	0·5
A in man-days per acre	1	0	2	0
L acres of land	1	1	1	1

This data table can be looked upon as an input-output table of requirements of resources, M, A and L.

Let x_1, x_2, x_3 and x_4 be the quantities of C, corn, O, oats, G, grass and W, wheat, respectively produced in one season, under a particular system of farming. These quantities are sometimes called the activity levels. There are three unalterable restrictions on our farming system, firstly, there are only 100 acres of L, land available on the farm for our crops, secondly, only 100 hours of labour M, available in the month of March, and thirdly there are only 80 hours of labour A, available in the month of August. So we have the three restrictions on our system;

$$100 \leqslant 1x_1 + 1x_2 + 1x_3 + 1x_4$$
$$100 \leqslant 0x_1 + 1x_2 + 0x_3 + 0·5x_4 \qquad (3.5.1)$$
$$80 \leqslant 1x_1 + 0x_2 + 2x_3 + 0x_4 \ .$$

The object of the calculation is to find that combination of the four crops C, O, G and W which will produce the maximum profit in one season. This profit z_0 which we wish to maximize is

$$z_0 = 30x_1 + 10x_2 + 40x_3 + 12x_4,$$

where the coefficients are expressed in terms of the net profit per acre of each crop; so that the first term is £30 $\times x_1$, the net profit from an acreage x_1 of corn, and so on. Firstly, we must get rid of the inequalities in the set of relations above. To do this, we introduce three extra variables x_5, x_6 and x_7. These are sometimes called 'dummy' or 'slack' variables as they represent the excess of our resources over our needs, and they can be thought of as taking up the slack arising from non-use of some of our resources. For example, it may be more profitable not to use all the land available, and then x_5 is a measure of the land not used. The problem is then expressed correctly in the standard simplex style:

Maximize $z = 30x_1 + 10x_2 + 40x_3 + 12x_4 + 0x_5 + 0x_6 + 0x_7$

under the constraints

$$100 = 1x_1 + 1x_2 + 1x_3 + 1x_4 + 1x_5 + 0x_6 + 0x_7$$
$$100 = 0x_1 + 1x_2 + 0x_3 + 0{\cdot}5x_4 + 0x_5 + 1x_6 + 0x_7 \qquad (3.5.2)$$
$$80 = 1x_1 + 0x_2 + 2x_3 + 0x_4 + 0x_5 + 0x_6 + 1x_7$$

We shall assume that every x is positive, that is, that there is no penalty or cost attaching to any non-use of resources. The first step in the calculation is to find any solution of our problem at all, that is to find any possible plan for running the farm, which satisfies the three constraints. Such a plan is called a feasible solution. Obviously we can just sit back and do nothing, that is, we can make no profit and make no use of our resources, so that one feasible solution is

$$x_1 = x_2 = x_3 = x_4 = 0, \quad x_5 = x_6 = x_7 = 1 \quad \text{and then} \quad z = 0.$$

This is the worst possible position, from the point of view of making a profit, so let us try the effect of producing some crop on some acres of our land.

The computing matrix for this first plan is:

Plan 1.	z	C	O	G	W	IL	IML	IAL	ratio
Revenue	0	0	0	0	0	0	0	0	
R_{-1}	−280	−2	−2	(−3)	−1·5	−1	−1	−1	
Revenue − cost	0	−30	−10	−40	−12	0	0	0	
L	100	1	1	1	1	1	0	0	100/1
ML	100	0	1	0	0·5	0	1	0	∞
AL	80	1	0	(2)	0	0	0	1	(80/2)

The best crop to start growing is that which produces the largest profit when grown on its own, so we seek along the R_{-1} row, and find that G, grass is the crop which produces the maximum profit (£40 per acre) when grown on its own. G has the largest negative element on the R_{-1} row, so we choose the G column as our pivot column, that is, we decide to bring the activity of growing grass into our farming system. But grass makes the greatest use of August labour, which is one of the constraints of our system, so there is an upper limit to the amount of grass which can be grown on our farm, and an upper limit to the profit we can make if we grow only grass. We see that August labour has the least positive ratio of the first column to the column G. If we select now another activity which uses little or no August labour, we can increase our profit by bringing this new activity into our plan as well as growing grass. To discover the most restricting of the three constraints, we choose that constraint which has the least positive ratio of the items in the z column, the profit column, to the items in the G column, the grass column. The selected ratio is in fact 80/2, so the pivot element is 2, and using this item as the pivot, we can now transform the whole matrix by the simplex process, in order to produce a new plan with increased profit. The selected constraint is August labour, and the new plan is:

Plan 2.	z	C	O	AL	W	IL	IML	IAL	ratio
R_{-1}	−160	−0·5	(−2)	1·5	−1·5	−1	−1	0·5	
Revenue − cost	1600	−10	−10	20	−12	0	0	20	
L	60	0·5	(1)	−0·5	1	1	0	−0·5	(60/1)
ML	100	0	1	0	0·5	0	1	0	100/1
G	40	0·5	0	0·5	0	0	0	0·5	∞

Here we use all our August labour to produce 40 acres of grass at a profit of £1600. We use no March labour and we have 60 acres of land left idle. Again we seek the maximum negative item along the first row, to find which activity to bring into the plan. We divide the first column by this column and select the least positive of the ratios, to find which constraint to remove from the plan. Here −2 is the most negative item in the first row, so we decide to bring in growing Oats as a new activity, and to use up the rest of the land on this, that is to remove land from the unused resources. We repeat the transformation of the whole matrix to produce a better plan again:

Plan 3.	z	C	L	AL	W	IL	IML	IAL	ratio
	−40	0·5	2	0·5	0·5	1	−1	−0·5	
	2200	−5	10	15	−2	10	0	15	
O	60	0·5	1	−0·5	1	1	0	−0·5	60/0 = ∞
ML	40	−0·5	−1	0·5	−0·5	−1	(1)	0·5	40/1
G	40	0·5	0	0·5	0	0	0	0·5	40/0 = ∞

Here we grow Oats as well on the remaining 60 acres of land and use some of the March labour to do it. We increase our profit to £2200 and we still have 40 hours of March labour unused.

There is now only one negative quantity left in the first row, −1 in the IML column, so we select this, form our ratios and transform our matrix as before, to produce :

Plan 4.	z	C	L	AL	W	IL	ML	IAL	ratio
	0	0	1	1	0	0	1	0	
	2200	(−5)	10	15	−2	10	0	15	
O	60	0·5	1	−0·5	1	1	0	−0·5	60/0·5
IML	40	−0·5	−1	0·5	−0·5	−1	1	0·5	
G	40	(0·5)	0	0·5	0	0	0	0·5	40/0·5

This is substantially the same as plan three, but we are now at the critical point explained above, when the first row is reduced to zeros and ones, and unused March labour has been brought into its proper position in the basic solution.

We go on testing on the second row, for the largest negative item in those columns which have a zero in the first row, we find −5 in the Corn column, and we find that grass has the least positive ratio, so it is the least profitable activity of those in the plan. We decide to introduce Corn and remove Grass from our plan. We pivot again and we find:

Plan 5.	z	G	L	AL	W	IL	ML	IAL	ratio
	0	0	1	1	0	0	1	0	
	2600	10	10	20	(−2)	10	0	20	
O	20	−1	1	−1	(1)	1	0	−1	20/1
IML	80	1	−1	1	−0·5	−1	1	1	
C	80	2	0	1	0	0	0	1	∞

There is now only one negative item in the second row, −2, so we pivot for the last time to remove oats from our plan and introduce wheat instead. We have finally:

Plan 6.	z	G	L	AL	O	IL	ML	IAL
	0	0	1	1	0	0	1	0
	2640	8	12	18	2	12	0	18
W	20	−1	1	−1	1	1	0	−1
IML	90	0·5	−0·5	0·5	0·5	−0·5	1	0·5
C	80	2	0	1	0	0	0	1

All the numbers in the second row are now positive, so that no new plan can be found to increase the profit above £2640 however we combine the crops. The final plan, when expressed in words is:- to grow twenty acres of wheat and eighty acres of corn on all of the hundred acres of land. We use all of the eighty hours of August labour but we have used only 10 of the hundred hours of March labour. The original first column represented resources of 100 acres of land, 100 hours of March labour and eighty hours of August labour. These have been transformed by the final plan into 20 acres of wheat, 80 acres of corn and 90 unused hours of March labour, with a profit of £2640. This example was proposed by Dr. A.M.M. McFarquhar of the Department of Agricultural Economics, Cambridge.

SECTION 2

A PROGRAM FOR LINEAR PROGRAMMING BY THE CONTRACTED SIMPLEX PROCESS

§3.6 Specification of program LP3A

This program minimizes

$$C = \sum_{v=0}^{n-m-1} c_v x_v$$

given m constraints of the forms

$$b_u \geqslant \sum_{v=0}^{n-m-1} a_{uv} x_v,$$

or

$$b_u = \sum_{v=0}^{n-m-1} a_{uv} x_v, \quad \text{for} \quad u = 0, 1, 2, \ldots, m-1,$$

and all

$$b_u, \ x_v \geqslant 0, \quad \text{for} \quad m \leqslant 50, \quad n - m \leqslant 50, \quad n > m.$$

It uses the contracted simplex process due to Prinz, that is to say, the "slack" variables are suppressed in the matrix. The program has five sections:

(i) *Input.* It reads in data in this form, where A is a code number to identify the data, M is the number of rows and N is the number of columns in input data, ($D = 0$ for $\geqslant$, or $D = 1$ for $=$).

A

$M \ N$

$C, \ c_0, \ c_1, \ c_2, \ \ldots, \ c_{n-m-1}$

$D_0, \ b_0, \ a_{00}, \ a_{01}, \ a_{02}, \ \ldots, \ a_{0,n-m-1}$

$D_1, \ b_1, \ a_{10}, \ a_{11}, \ a_{12}, \ \ldots, \ a_{1,n-m-1}$

$D_2, \ b_2, \ a_{20}, \ a_{21}, \ a_{22}, \ \ldots, \ a_{2,n-m-1}$

$\cdots\cdots$

$D_m, \ b_{m-1}, \ a_{m-1,0}, \ a_{m-1,1}, \ a_{m-1,2}, \ \ldots, \ a_{m-1,n-m-1}$

$-1 \ -1$ to stop run

or -1 to read next set of data.

It sets up the matrix

v_{-1}	v_0	v_1	$\cdots$	v_{n-m-1}	(Row R_{-1})
C	c_0	c_1	$\cdots$	c_{n-m-1}	(Row R_0)
b_0	a_{00}	a_{01}	$\cdots$		(Row R_1)
b_1	a_{10}	a_{11}	$\cdots$		(Row R_2)
			$\cdots\cdots$		
b_{m-1}	$a_{m-1,0}$	$a_{m-1,1}$	$\cdots$	$a_{m-1,n-m-1}$	(Row R_m)

125

where $C = 0$ initially, and row R_{-1} consists of the sums of the columns of the matrix, excluding row R_0, each multiplied by its own D_m. That is

$$v_{-1} = b_0 + b_1 + \ldots + b_{m-1},$$

$$v_0 = a_{0,0} + a_{1,0} + \ldots + a_{m-1,0}$$

and so on.

It also sets up the J row as $1, 2, \ldots, (n-m)$, $(n-m$ items) to represent the suffixes of these variables not in the initial basis, and the I column as $101, \ldots, 100 + m$, $(m$ items) to represent the suffixes of those "slack" variables which form the initial basis for a solution.

(ii) *The K section.* This section finds which variable x_k is the best one to introduce into the basis. It first tests if the so-called "critical point" has been reached in the calculation, by testing all the addresses in the I column. If any is > 100, the program goes on to the main K sequence, but if all are < 100 every element of the row R_{-1} (which at this critical point contains approximate 0's and 1's only) is replaced by an exact 1 if the corresponding J index is > 100, and an exact 0, otherwise. This is to prevent the program getting into an infinite cycle at this point, due to accumulated rounding errors. When once this point has been reached a switch order is set in the program to ignore this test in future cycles.

The main part of the K section seeks along the rows R_{-1} and R_0, to find the greatest negative v_j, or if all the v_j's are > 0, the greatest negative c_j, from those columns which have $v_j = 0$. If all the v_j's are > 0, and there is no negative c_j left, the process of minimizing is finished and the program jumps to the final print sequence. If however the greatest negative v_j (or c_j) occurs in column C_S, then S is the address in the J row of the suffix k of the best variable to introduce into the basis. The program prints k, and goes on to the next section.

(iii) *The R section.* This section finds which variable x_r is the best one to remove from the basis.

It forms the m ratios t_u, by dividing the element in column C_k by that in C_{-1}, and seeks the least positive t_u, t_R, where R is the address in the I column of the suffix r of the best variable x_r to be removed from the basis.

It prints the selected t_R and r.

(iv) *The X section.* This section transforms the entire matrix including column C_{-1}, and rows R_0 and R_{-1}, by the rules

$$x'_{rk} = 1/x_{rk}, \text{ for the pivot } x_{rk},$$

$$x'_{rs} = x_{rs}/x_{rk}, \ s \neq k, \text{ for the main column, } C_r,$$

$$x'_{uk} = -x_{uk}/x_{rk}, \ u \neq r, \text{ for the main row, } R_k,$$

and $$x'_{us} = x_{us} - x_{rs}\, x_{uk}/x_{rk}, \ u \neq r, \ s \neq k,$$

for all the rest of the matrix.

It also exchanges k from the Sth place in the J row and r from the Rth place in the I column.

Then the program goes back to the start of section (ii) to do another cycle.

126

(v) *Final print sequence.* When all possible cycles have been completed the program prints the contents of the row R_0 and the column C_{-1}, of the main matrix. These elements are the final values of $b_0, b_1, ..., b_{m-1}$, together with the numbers in the I row and the final J column, which form the suffixes of the x's inside and outside the final basic solution.

§3.7 Flow diagram for LP3A

LP3A: Master routine.

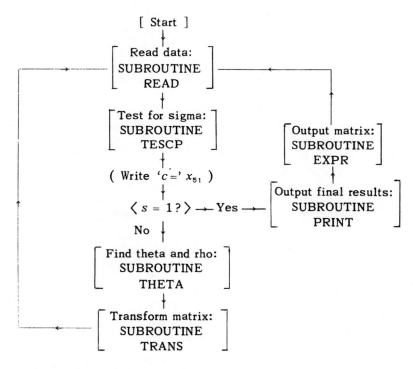

LP3A: Subroutine: READ, Reads and checks data, sets up initial matrix.

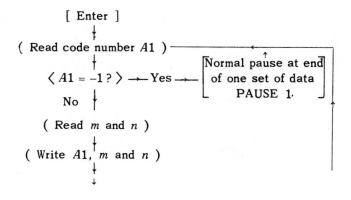

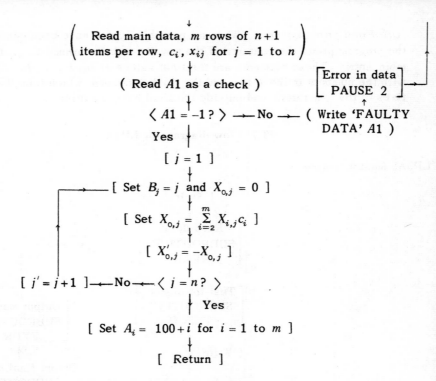

$$\left(\begin{array}{c} \text{Read main data, } m \text{ rows of } n+1 \\ \text{items per row, } c_i, x_{ij} \text{ for } j = 1 \text{ to } n \end{array} \right)$$

(Read $A1$ as a check)

$\left[\begin{array}{c} \text{Error in data} \\ \text{PAUSE } 2 \end{array} \right]$

$\langle A1 = -1 ? \rangle$ —— No —— (Write 'FAULTY DATA' $A1$)

Yes

$[j = 1]$

$[$ Set $B_j = j$ and $X_{0,j} = 0]$

$[$ Set $X_{0,j} = \sum_{i=2}^{m} X_{i,j} c_i]$

$[X'_{0,j} = -X_{0,j}]$

$[j' = j+1]$ —— No —— $\langle j = n ? \rangle$

Yes

$[$ Set $A_i = 100 + i$ for $i = 1$ to $m]$

$[$ Return $]$

LP3A: Subroutine: TESCP. Seeks greatest negative c_j or v_j.

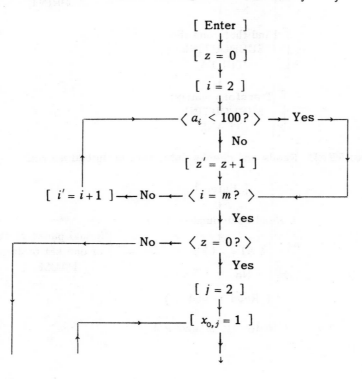

$[$ Enter $]$

$[z = 0]$

$[i = 2]$

$\langle a_i < 100 ? \rangle$ —— Yes ——

No

$[z' = z+1]$

$[i' = i+1]$ —— No —— $\langle i = m ? \rangle$

Yes

No —— $\langle z = 0 ? \rangle$

Yes

$[j = 2]$

$[x_{0,j} = 1]$

128

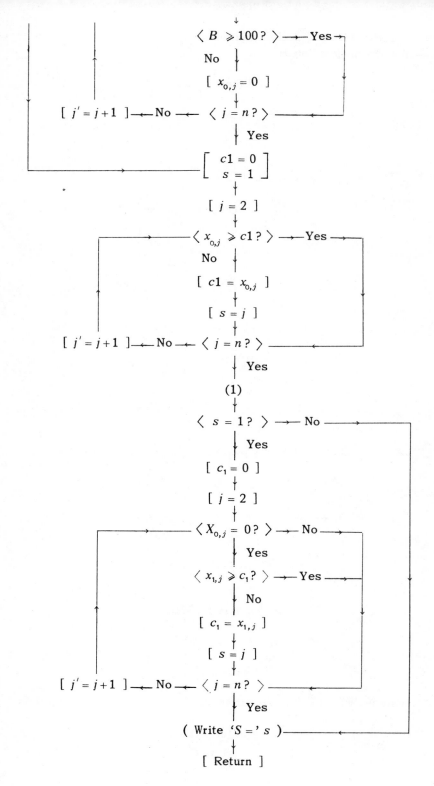

⟨ B ⩾ 100? ⟩ ——— Yes —

No ↓

[$x_{0,j} = 0$]

[$j' = j+1$] ——No—— ⟨ $j = n$? ⟩

↓ Yes

$\begin{bmatrix} c1 = 0 \\ s = 1 \end{bmatrix}$

[$j = 2$]

⟨ $x_{0,j} \geqslant c1$? ⟩ ——— Yes —

No ↓

[$c1 = x_{0,j}$]

[$s = j$]

[$j' = j+1$] ——No—— ⟨ $j = n$? ⟩

↓ Yes

(1)

⟨ $s = 1$? ⟩ ——— No

↓ Yes

[$c_1 = 0$]

[$j = 2$]

⟨ $X_{0,j} = 0$? ⟩ ——— No

↓ Yes

⟨ $x_{1,j} \geqslant c_1$? ⟩ ——— Yes

↓ No

[$c_1 = x_{1,j}$]

[$s = j$]

[$j' = j+1$] ——No—— ⟨ $j = n$? ⟩

↓ Yes

(Write 'S =' s)

↓

[Return]

LP3A: Subroutine: THETA. Seeks least positive ratio t_R to determine which x_r to remove from the basic solution.

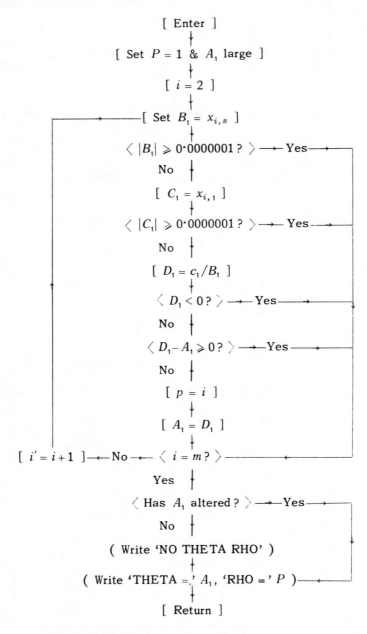

[Enter]

[Set $P = 1$ & A_1 large]

[$i = 2$]

[Set $B_1 = x_{i,s}$]

⟨ $|B_1| \geqslant 0 \cdot 0000001$? ⟩ —— Yes ——

No

[$C_1 = x_{i,1}$]

⟨ $|C_1| \geqslant 0 \cdot 0000001$? ⟩ —— Yes ——

No

[$D_1 = c_1/B_1$]

⟨ $D_1 < 0$? ⟩ —— Yes ——

No

⟨ $D_1 - A_1 \geqslant 0$? ⟩ —— Yes ——

No

[$p = i$]

[$A_1 = D_1$]

[$i' = i + 1$] —— No —— ⟨ $i = m$? ⟩

Yes

⟨ Has A_1 altered ? ⟩ —— Yes ——

No

(Write 'NO THETA RHO')

(Write 'THETA =' A_1, 'RHO =' P)

[Return]

LP3A: Subroutine: TRANS. Transforms whole matrix by the simplex process.

[Enter]

130

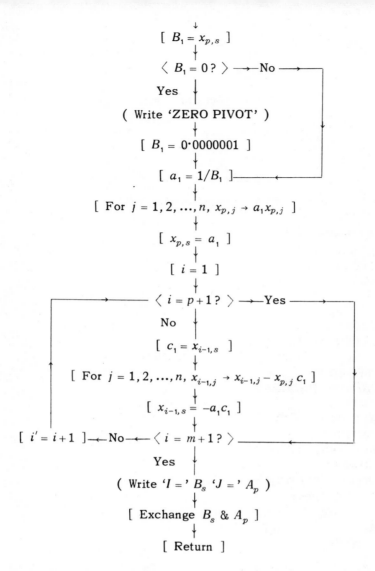

$$[\ B_1 = x_{p,s}\ ]$$

$$\langle\ B_1 = 0\,?\ \rangle \longrightarrow \text{No} \longrightarrow$$

Yes

$$(\ \text{Write 'ZERO PIVOT'}\ )$$

$$[\ B_1 = 0{\cdot}0000001\ ]$$

$$[\ a_1 = 1/B_1\ ]$$

$$[\ \text{For}\ j = 1, 2, ..., n,\ x_{p,j} \to a_1 x_{p,j}\ ]$$

$$[\ x_{p,s} = a_1\ ]$$

$$[\ i = 1\ ]$$

$$\langle\ i = p+1\,?\ \rangle \longrightarrow \text{Yes} \longrightarrow$$

No

$$[\ c_1 = x_{i-1,s}\ ]$$

$$[\ \text{For}\ j = 1, 2, ..., n,\ x_{i-1,j} \to x_{i-1,j} - x_{p,j}\, c_1\ ]$$

$$[\ x_{i-1,s} = -a_1 c_1\ ]$$

$$[\ i' = i+1\ ] \longleftarrow \text{No} \longleftarrow \langle\ i = m+1\,?\ \rangle$$

Yes

$$(\ \text{Write}\ 'I =\,'\ B_s\ 'J =\,'\ A_p\ )$$

$$[\ \text{Exchange}\ B_s\ \&\ A_p\ ]$$

$$[\ \text{Return}\ ]$$

LP3A: Subroutine: PRINT. Prints the final basic solution.

$$[\ \text{Enter}\ ]$$

$$(\ \text{For}\ i = 1\ \text{to}\ m,\ \text{write}\ 'I =\,'\ a_i\ 'X =\,'\ x_{i,1}\ )$$

$$(\ \text{For}\ j = 1\ \text{to}\ n,\ \text{write}\ 'J =\,'\ b_j\ 'X =\,'\ x_{1,j}\ )$$

$$(\ \text{Write}\ '\text{FINAL}\ C\ \text{IS}'\ X_{1,1}\ )$$

$$[\ \text{Return}\ ]$$

LP3A: Subroutine: EXPR. Prints the final matrix.

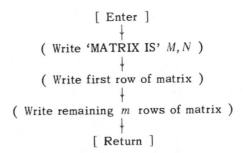

[Enter]
↓
(Write 'MATRIX IS' M, N)
↓
(Write first row of matrix)
↓
(Write remaining m rows of matrix)
↓
[Return]

§3.8 Fortran program LP3A

```
        PROGRAM (LP3A)
        INPUT 1 = TR0
        OUTPUT 2 = LP0
        END


        MASTER LP3A
C       SLATER SIMPLEX 11.7.66
        COMMON // A(50), B(50), C(50), X(2600)
        INTEGER R,S
C       STEERING PROGRAM
1       CONTINUE
        CALL READ (M,N)
98      CONTINUE
        CALL TESCP (C1,S,M,N,)
101     FORMAT (/5H C = , F14·5)
        WRITE (2,101) X(51)
        IF (S − 1) 0,99,0
        CALL THETA (A1,R,M,S)
        CALL TRANS (M,N,R,S)
        GO TO 98

99      CALL PRINT (M,N)
        CALL EXPR (M,N)
        GO TO 1

        END

        SUBROUTINE READ (M,N)
C       READ AND CHECK DATA
        COMMON // A(50), B(50), C(50), X(2600)
        INTEGER R,S

102     FORMAT (E0)
14      READ (1,102) A1
```

```
C         PAUSE IF A1 = –1
          IF (A1 + 1·0) 103,0,103
          PAUSE 1
          GO TO 14

104       FORMAT (2I0)
103       READ (1, 104) M,N
105       FORMAT (50E0)
106       FORMAT (/ F14·5,I3,I3)
          WRITE (2, 106) A1,M,N
          DO 107 I = 1,M
          READ (1,105) C(I), (X(I*50 + J), J = 1,N)
107       CONTINUE
C         READ –1 AS CHECK
          READ (1,102) A1
          IF (A1 + 1·0) 0,108,0
109       FORMAT (/12H FAULTY DATA, F14·5)
          WRITE (2,109) A1
          PAUSE 2
          GO TO 14

108       DO 119 J = 1,N
          B(J) = J
          X(J) = 0
          DO 110 I = 2,M
110       X(J) = X(J + 50*I)*C(I) + X(J)
119       X(J) = –X(J)
          DO 111 I = 1,M
111       A(I) = I + 100
          RETURN
          END


          SUBROUTINE TESCP (C1,S,M,N,)
C         TEST FOR CRITICAL POINT AND SEEK X(K), SIGMA
          COMMON // A(50), B(50), C(50), X(2600)
          INTEGER R,S

          Z = 0
          DO 20 I = 2,M
          IF (A(I) – 100·0) 20,0,0
          Z = Z + 1·0
20        CONTINUE
          IF (Z) 21,0,21
          DO 22 J = 2,N
          X(J) = 1·0
          IF (B(J) – 100·0) 0,22,22
          X(J) = 0
22        CONTINUE
21        C1 = 0
```

133

```
           S = 1
           DO 23 J = 2,N
           IF (X(J) − C1 ) 0,23,23
           C1 = X(J)
           S = J
23         CONTINUE
           IF (S − 1) 24,0,24
           C1 = 0
           DO 25 J = 2,N
           IF (X(J)) 25,0,25
           IF (X(J + 50) − C1) 0,25,25
           C1 = X(J + 50)
           S = J
25         CONTINUE
24         WRITE (2,50) S
50         FORMAT (/5H S = , I3)
           RETURN
           END


           SUBROUTINE THETA (A1,R,M,S)
C          FIND THETA AND RHO
           COMMON / / A(50), B(50), C(50), X(2600)
           INTEGER R,S

           R = 1
           A1 = 100000000·0
           DO 30 I = 2,M
           B1 = X(50*I + S)
           B2 = 1E−7 − ABS(B1)
           IF (B2) 0,30,30
           C1 = X(50*I + 1)
           C2 = 1E−7 − ABS(C1)
           D1 = C1/B1
           IF (D1) 30,0,0
           IF (D1 − A1) 0,30,30
           R = I
           A1 = D1
30         CONTINUE
           IF (A1 − 100000000·0) 31,0,31
32         FORMAT (/13H NO THETA RHO, F14·5)
           WRITE (2,32) A1
33         FORMAT (/9H THETA = , F14·5, 6H RHO = , I3)
31         WRITE (2,33) A1,R
           RETURN
           END


           SUBROUTINE TRANS (M,N,R,S)
C          TRANSFORM MATRIX BY SIMPLEX PROCESS
```

```
          COMMON / / A(50), B(50), C(50), X(2600)
          INTEGER R,S

          B1 = X(50*R + S)
          IF (B1) 40,0,40
42        FORMAT (/11H ZERO PIVOT, I3)
          WRITE (2,42) R
          B1 = 0·000001
40        A1 = 1·0/B1
          DO 43 J = 1,N
43        X(J + 50*R) = A1*X(J + 50*R)
          X(S + 50*R) = A1
          M1 = M + 1
          DO 41 I = 1,M1
          IF (I − 1 − R) 0,41,0
          I1 = 50*I + S − 50
          C1 = X(I1)
          DO 45 J = 1,N
          I2 = 50*I + J − 50
45        X(I2) = X(I2) − X(50*R + J)*C1
          X(I1) = − A1*C1
41        CONTINUE
47        FORMAT (/5H I = , F5·0, 5H J = , F5·0)
          WRITE (2,47) B(S), A(R)
          D1 = B(S)
          B(S) = A(R)
          A(R) = D1
          RETURN
          END

          SUBROUTINE PRINT (M,N)
C         PRINT FINAL RESULT
          COMMON / / A(50), B(50), C(50), X(2600)
          INTEGER R,S
51        FORMAT (/5H I = , F5·0, 5H X = , F14·5)
          WRITE (2,51) (A(I), X(50*I + 1), I = 1,M)
52        FORMAT (/5H J = , F5·0, 5H X = , F14·5)
          WRITE (2,52) (B(J), X(50 + J), J = 1,N)
53        FORMAT (/ / 12H FINAL C IS , F14·5)
          WRITE (2,53) X(51)
          RETURN
          END

          SUBROUTINE EXPR (M,N)
C         EXTRA PRINTING
          COMMON / / A(50), B(50), C(50), X(2600)
          INTEGER R,S
6         FORMAT (/ 11H MATRIX IS , 2I3)
```

```
        WRITE (2,6) M,N
7       FORMAT (5 F14·5)
        WRITE (2,7) (X(J), J = 1,N)
        DO 8 I = 1,M
        WRITE (2,7) (X(I*50+J), J = 1,N)
8       CONTINUE
        RETURN
        END

        FINISH
```

§3.9 Sample of input and output of LP3A

Input data.

5·1						Code number to identify the set of data.			
8	17					Size of data followed by data matrix in rows.			
0	0	0	0	0	−1	−1	−1	−1	−1
−1	−1	−1	−1	−1	0·147		2000	−1500	
1	1	0	0	3·87	1·04	0·46	0·55	0·34	1·90
0	0	0	2·29	0	0	−2290	−2290		
1	1	0	0	0·95	1·76	0·61	0·17	0·51	1·22
0	1·68	0·63	0·84	6·32	0	−2100	−2100		
1	1	0	0	3·30	0	0	29·85	0	0
89·55	0	0	0	0	0	−750	−750		
1	1	0	0	1·17	3·44	3·50	0·49	0·65	3·25
0·05	6·30	1·23	1·30	0·46	−1	−680	−680		
1	1	0	0	0·11	1·79	2·57	0·55	0·83	0·15
0·05	0·91	1·82	0·44	0	0	−130	−130		
1	1	0	0	0·85	0·38	0·28	0·28	0·14	0·96
1·01	0·92	0·69	0·92	8·42	0	−2290	−2290		
1	1	0	0	2·76	2·04	3·51	0·73	0·10	1·46
0·91	2·73	1·21	0·91	0	0	−1520	−1520		
−1									
−1						Terminating symbols at which size of data is checked.			

Output results.

```
        5·100000            8               17          Code number and size of data.
S =  10  C =            0·00000 THETA =            0·01117  RHO = 4
I = 10. J  = 104.
S =  14  C =            0·01117 THETA =            0·11743  RHO = 7
I = 14. J  = 107.
S =  11  C =            0·12859 THETA =            0·15127  RHO = 5
I = 11. J  = 105.
```

S = 4 C =	0·26334 THETA =	0·25803 RHO = 8
I = 4. J = 108.		
S = 5 C =	0·18759 THETA =	0·01495 RHO = 2
I = 5. J = 102.		
S = 16 C =	0·19566 THETA =	0·00008 RHO = 3
I = 16. J = 103.		
S = 13 C =	0·09287 THETA =	0·00611 RHO = 4
I = 13. J = 10.		
S = 6 C =	–0·14826 THETA =	0·02308 RHO = 5
I = 6. J = 11.		

One row is printed like this for each transformation of the matrix. It shows which variable is coming in to the solution and which variable is going out of the solution at each complete cycle.

S = 13 C =	–0·27267 THETA =	0·00576 RHO = 3
I = 10. J = 16.		
S = 12 C =	0·39426 THETA =	0·19101 RHO = 5
I = 12. J = 6.		
S = 15 C =	0·50858 THETA =	0·32101 RHO = 8
I = 15. J = 4.		
S = 13 C =	0·84490 THETA =	0·00001 RHO = 6
I = 16. J = 106.		
S = 17 C =	0·83855 THETA =	0·47853 RHO = 6
I = 17. J = 16.		
S = 6 C =	0·87087 THETA =	0·47853 RHO = 5
I = 11. J = 12.		
S = 9 C =	3·61778 THETA =	0·01357 RHO = 2
I = 9. J = 5.		
S = 15 C =	3·65445 THETA =	2·09189 RHO = 5
I = 4. J = 11.		
S = 1 C =	27·72001	
I = 101. X =	27·72001	Final solution vectors,
I = 9. X =	7·82954	the first column of the
I = 10. X =	0·03715	final matrix and the
I = 13. X =	2·71255	cost row of the final
I = 4. X =	2·09191	matrix.
I = 17. X =	0·01231	
I = 14. X =	2·06133	
I = 15. X =	23·00110	
J = 1. X =	27·72001	
J = 2. X =	0·00000	
J = 3. X =	0·00000	
J = 108. X =	13·58410	

$J = 102.\ X =$ −9·42222
$J = 12.\ X =$ 62·26221
$J = 7.\ X =$ 11·69445
$J = 8.\ X =$ 14·63889
$J = 5.\ X =$ 48·36001
$J = 104.\ X =$ −0·23532
$J = 105.\ X =$ 0·14700
$J = 6.\ X =$ 106·00991
$J = 106.\ X =$ 26·25889
$J = 107.\ X =$ 8·30756
$J = 11.\ X =$ 50·20402
$J = 103.\ X =$ −10·92012
$J = 16.\ X =$ 3500·00000

FINAL C IS   27·2001

Further reading on linear programming will be found in:

> Blackwell and Girshik (1954),
> Charnes, Cooper and Henderson (1953),
> Gass (1958),
> Heady and Candler (1958)

and   Vajda (1958).

4 SURVEY ANALYSIS

SECTION 1

HOW TO DO A SIMPLE SURVEY

§4.1 Asking the right questions

The process of carrying out a survey analysis can be greatly simplified if certain basic principles are understood and acted upon. The first rule in doing any survey is not to collect any data until all the details of the survey, the questions to be asked, the layout of the forms, and the coding onto cards of the replies have all been finally settled.

A survey is the collection and processing of data in order to find out some facts about the population from which come the people actually questioned. The objectives of the survey should be quite clearly formulated at the start of the survey. It is only too easy to ask irrelevant questions and collect unnecessarily large sets of data, in the hope that the answers might come in useful, sometime in the future.

Once the objectives have been clearly and precisely stated, the form of the actual questions that are to be asked must be decided. Also we must decide if the questions are to be asked by an interviewer or if the form is to be filled by the person being questioned, that is by the respondent. At this point the need to process the answers through a computer intrudes itself on the surveyist. All answers to questions must be capable of being coded in a precise numerical or alphabetical form, so that they can be punched onto cards, ready to be input to a computer. With a small computer, the alphabetic form of coding replies should be avoided.

When we have decided what questions we want to ask, we have to decide next the precise wording of every question. The answers to questions fall into two natural types, the integer type requiring one reply only from a series of fixed possible answers, and the quantitative type requiring an actual numerical quantity as its answer.

As an example of the quantitative type, we might have the question:-

How many bedrooms has your house?

This could have any answer such as 1, 2, 3 up to even 50 in an extreme case. It is better rephrased as a series of integer type questions,

How many bedrooms has your house, one? ☐ 5/1

two? ☐ 5/2

three?		5/3

four?		5/4

more than four?		5/5

Please tick one box only.

The forms on which the answers are to be entered should be laid out as clearly as possible. No attempt should be made to save space. Every question should have some boxes to the right of the question for the answer. These boxes should be under one another so that when the data comes to be punched onto cards, the card puncher's eyes can travel easily down the column. The numbers of the card columns into which the answers are to be punched can also be printed on the form to the far right of the questions and the answer boxes. As an example, suppose we want to find out if a person with red hair is taller than someone with hair of another colour. This is the objective of our survey. We might then prepare a hundred forms in the layout:

Name . . . .

Address . . . .

Age . . . .

Height . . . .

Colour of hair . . . .

This is how not to do it. The answers filled in by people for themselves would be in long-hand and difficult to code up. The name and address are only useful to deduce the sex of the respondent; indeed if the questions are at all personal such as:

What is your annual income?

truthful replies will only be given if the name and address are not asked.
A much better layout would be:

Form number		1/2/3

1)   Are you male?   4/0

        or female?   4/1

2)   Are you under 14 years old?   ☐   5/0

         Between 14 and 21?   ☐   5/1

         Over 21?   ☐   5/2

3)   Is red the natural colour of your hair?   Yes   ☐   6/0

         No   ☐   6/1

4)   What is your height without shoes?   Under 5 ft.   ☐   7/0

         Between 5 ft. and 5' 6"?   ☐   7/1

         Between 5'6" and 6 ft?   ☐   7/2

         Over 6 ft?   ☐   7/3

     The form number can be filled in before the form is sent out. Only a quick scan for completeness is needed at the coding stage, and the position in the card for each item is clearly shown.

     Answers which go in one column are shown as boxes vertically under one another. Answers which go in separate columns on a card are shown as horizontal separate boxes.

     Numerical answers may need to be processed by the computer. Thus a question such as:

         What is your height? ☐ ft. ☐☐ ins.   12/13/14

may need to be expressed in inches before anything else can be done with it. To avoid this, the question can often be rephrased into a grouped integer response as in the last question above.

     There are many ways in which questions can be asked. The actual wording of every question must be as simple, clear and precise as possible. Slang, foreign, obscure or unusual words must be avoided. So must ambiguities, longwinded phrasing, and any wording in a question which might cause embarassment and lead to untruthful replies. The classic example here is:

"What class do you belong to?"	Upper?		7/0
	Middle?		7/1
	Working?		7/2

Very few respondents will admit to belonging to the upper class or to the working class. The question is better rephrased:

"What class do you belong to?"	Upper class?		7/0
	Upper middle class?		7/1
	Lower middle class?		7/2
	Working class?		7/3

In this second case the question is more likely to be answered truthfully and the essential distinction of class will be shown more accurately in the replies, though probably still with a slight upward bias.

Just as there are many ways in which questions can be phrased, so there are many types of answer. From the point of view of processing the answers, the simple numerical or integer answers are the best, but sometimes it is not easy to see how to phrase a question to get such a simple answer.

A question such as

"Do you own a radio, a television set, a refrigerator,
an electric cooker?"

might provoke the uninformative answer, "Yes". In this case, the question asked may have several answers, and again it is better rephrased as a list of simple questions:

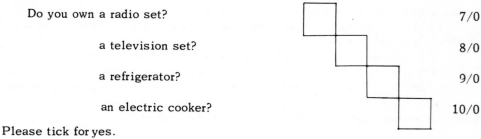

Do you own a radio set?		7/0
a television set?		8/0
a refrigerator?		9/0
an electric cooker?		10/0

Please tick for yes.

Here we have stepped boxes to one side to show the card punch operator that every answer must fall in a different column on the card. We try to avoid having more than one item of information in any one column on the card. Questions of opinion are usually the most difficult to phrase and code accurately.

A question such as:

"What do you think are the chief causes of indigestion?"

may provide an essay on the subject from an eager respondent; it is better phrased as:

"Which do you think are the chief causes of indigestion?"

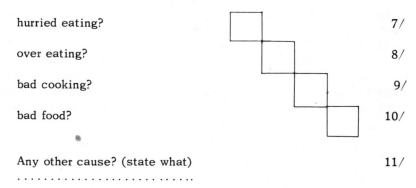

hurried eating?	7/
over eating?	8/
bad cooking?	9/
bad food?	10/
Any other cause? (state what)	11/

Please number in order of importance, 1 for the most important cause, down to 5 for the least important cause.

§4.2 Coding the replies

In order to use any computer to process the answers to our questions, all the data collected in the survey has to be punched onto cards, ready for input to the computer.

A punched card is an oblong card about the size of a post-card. The top left hand corner is cut off so that a pack of cards can be readily checked for any card which is back to front or upside down. Each card has 80 columns, numbered 1 to 80, on it. Each column has 12 possible positions into which an oblong hole can be punched. These positions are identified from the top of the card as U (upper), L (lower) and the 10 digits, 0, 1, ... 9. The two positions U and L are only rarely used alone. More usually they are combined with a digit hole to give two holes in one column, representing alphabetic and other simple symbols.

The position of any hole on a card can be identified by its column number and its row number. Thus the four corners of a card are

$$1/U, 80/U, 80/9 \text{ and } 1/9.$$

Each card is punched on a card-punching machine and then verified for accuracy on another machine called a verifier.

A complete pack of data cards must be handled with great care, stored in special boxes or trays, not crushed or bent, and not allowed to get dusty or damp. Obviously great care must be taken to keep the pack in its correct order, and in particular, not to drop the pack.

Each card should contain, usually in its first 6 columns, a code number giving the position of the card in the pack. The layout of the answers on a card is called the Format of the card.

Sometimes the answers on one form of a survey occupy more that the 80 columns available on one card. In this case, two or more cards are needed for a complete set of answers. Each card has a card type number, usually punched in column 80. In references, the card type number is placed before the column number. Thus 2.60/1 means the hole at position 1 of column 60 of card type 2. The columns occupied by one answer are called the data field, on the card for that answer. The whole set of answers on one form is called a record. Each separate answer may occupy several columns on a card, so each answer is given a number in its record.

For example a set of answers has 60 items in it. The first 50 items occupy one column each on a card but the remaining 10 items need five columns each, so $50 + 10 \times 5 = 100$ columns are needed in all. The items in the record are numbered 1 to 60. But the actual data occupies two cards. Card type 1 is in the format:

cols. 1 − 6 code name of record.

cols. 7 − 56 the 50 single digit items 1 to 50 of each record, occupying
50 single column fields on card 1.

col. 80 1, the card type
Card type 2 is in the different format.

cols. 1 − 6 code name of record.

cols. 7 − 56 the 10 five digit items 51 to 60 of each record occupying
10 five column fields on card 2.

col. 80 2, the card type.

The format for each card of each record is expressed in the normal Fortran format conventions, ready for input to the computer. Each data pack is preceded by one or more format cards giving the layout of the complete record. In the above example the format cards would be

(I1, A5, 50 I1, 22 X, I1/

I1, A5, 10 I5, 22 X, I1)

Here A5 means 5 columns of alphabetic or numeric data, which can be printed immediately, to give proof that all cards went into the computer in the correct order. 50 I1 means 50 integer items occupying one column each, 22 X means 22 items occupying one column each, to be ignored, 10 I5, means 10 items occupying 5 columns each, of which the last two columns can be considered to be after the decimal point.

The A, I, X descriptors are the only symbols which need to be used in describing the format of survey analysis cards. Numbers which are to be read in as numerical quantities must always be punched in the consecutive columns assigned to them on the card with the lowest digit in the column furthest to the right.

Any unused columns on the left are filled in with zeros.

144

Thus, suppose the question was —

What is your annual income?   £ | | | | |

10/11/12/13

and four answers were 2500, 950, 700 and none, these would be edited and entered into the code box as

2500, 0950, 0700, 0000

They would each be punched in the four columns 10 to 13 on the card.

The same size of field (in this case 4 columns) must be assigned in the same
position of each record even if the answer is zero.

Alphanumeric or double punching or anything which results in more than one
hole in any one column should be avoided, except in code names.

When the final layout of the question form has been decided, the final form of
the replies on each group of cards forming one record should be fairly obvious.
The reply boxes on the form should show how many cards are required for each
completed form of replies. Each numerical digit and each integer answer requires
one column on a card. The total number of columns is given by the total number
of boxes on the form and the columns into which the answers must be punched
are shown on the far right of each form. Of course, the answers must be arranged
on the cards in the same sequence as they are on the forms. It is not reasonable
to expect a card punch operator to punch the last ten columns of a card before
the first twenty.

The proposed layout of both forms and cards must be checked *very carefully
indeed* by someone other than their originator, for any slips, ambiguities or other
inclarities and imprecisions. Any mistakes at this preliminary stage can cost a
lot of wasted time and money. It is a good practice to have about 10 question-
naires filled in and punched as trial data, before the main operation, so that all
such points about clarity and layout of cards can be checked, and any mistakes
found out at the earliest possible moment.

§4.3 What to do with the data

When we have got all the answers to our questions coded onto the pack of
cards, there are several elementary calculations that we usually need to carry
out. First, we need to do straightforward counting of answers. If we use our previous example above, how many people answered in all, and how many of them
have red hair. If the record for each reply occupies several cards, we need to
count all the cards, usually by continuous adding of a single hole 1/1 in column
one, and divide the answer by the number of cards in each record. Next we count
the number of cards with an 0 hole in one column 6, such counting is called one
dimensional or 1D counting. It can be done on a counter sorter without any need
of a computer.

The question: What percentage of the respondents had red hair? can be answered. It is the total with red hair divided by the total number of replies. Such
simple percentages can be carried out on a hand calculator.

The next question might be: How many men have red hair? that is of all the cards of type 1 with a hole at 4/0, how many also have a hole at 6/0. This is a simple two dimensional or 2D integer count. Again such counts can be carried out on a counter sorter, but if there are many such counts to be made, it is probably quicker to use a computer. Let us tabulate the answers to question (1) against the answers to question (3) in our example on red hair.

There are four possible combinations of integer replies,

Male and red hair,	Female and red hair,
Holes at 4/0 and 6/0	Holes at 4/1 and 6/0
Males without red hair,	Females without red hair,
Holes in 4/0 and 6/1	Holes at 4/1 and 6/1

Thus we have a 2D table of answers of size 2×2. Each cell in the table contains a simple total of the number of people who satisfy the conditions of that cell, that is with that particular combination of holes on their cards.

The next extension is to a three dimensional or 3D table. Suppose we extend the above 2D table to one which consists of all possible combinations of males and females with or without red hair who are under 14, between 14 and 21 or over 21. We have a table consisting of 3 2×2 tables similar to the one above, and we have $3 \times 2 \times 2$ cells in this table, with holes at

4/0, 5/0, 6/0	4/1, 5/0, 6/0	4/0, 5/0, 6/1	4/1, 5/0, 6/1
4/0, 5/1, 6/0	4/1, 5/1, 6/0	4/0, 5/1, 6/1	4/1, 5/1, 6/1
4/0, 5/2, 6/0	4/1, 5/2, 6/0	4/0, 5/2, 6/1	4/1, 5/2, 6/1

Three dimensions is the most in which such sub-tabulations are usually made, since at each sub-tabulation the number of replies in each cell becomes progressively fewer. Again we can form row and column sums in all directions, and print percentages. So much for integer data.

The next type of calculation is the handling of numerical answers. Here we still need to count how many made a reply, but we also need to add up the actual numerical replies made.

In one dimension, this is the sum of the answers to one question on each record. This sum normally has to be divided by the total of answers to form an average answer.

Thus if 4 men replied that their incomes were £2,500, £1,500, £950 and £750 respectively the average income would be

$$(2500 + 1500 + 950 + 750)/4 = £1,425$$

Again the counting can be done in one, two or three dimensional tables.

Thus if the question on annual income were added to the form about red hair we might want to know the average annual income of all the females with red hair. This would involve forming two two-dimensional tables. In the first table each cell holds the sum of all the replies in that class. Again we form averages by dividing each sum in the second table by the number in the corresponding cell of the first table.

146

A SMALL SURVEY PROGRAM

§4.4 Specification of program SURV

Stage 1. This part of the program reads a pack of data cards in any integer format, onto a magnetic tape for storage. The data pack is preceded by some heading cards. Since the data consists of a number of records, and one complete record may occupy several cards, each card in the record may be in a different type of layout or format, but each complete record is in the same overall format. The cards for one complete record must be together in the data pack and in their correct order so that a card of type 1 is followed by a card of type 2 and so on.

Each record consists of a number of items of information, and each item of information can occupy several columns on a card. Each item of information is identified by the number of its position in the record, and not by the numbers of the columns it occupies on the card.

The first heading card is in this layout;

Col. 1.	0	
NAME	in columns 2 to 17.	This is the name of the pack of data, consisting of up to 16 letters.
M	in columns 18 to 20.	The total number of records in the data pack, $M \leqslant 999$.
N	in columns 21 to 23.	The total number of items in one record, $N \leqslant 100$.
K	in columns 24 to 26.	The total number of cards in one record, $K \leqslant 8$.

If $N = -1$, the program switches to the tables section without reading in any data. This facility is for use when the data pack is already on magnetic tape.

The remaining heading cards are one to $K \leqslant$ eight in number. They contain the formats for each type of card in any one record. The first format card has an opening bracket (in its first column, and the last format card has a closing bracket) as its last item, though not necessarily in its last column. The first item of each record is set automatically to unity. The data pack is followed by a closing card, punched with nines in columns one to thirty six. The program pauses at PAUSE 1 whenever such a card is read.

Example of layout of the data pack for SURV.

Card 1, heading card.

Col. 1	.Cols. 2 to 17	Col. 20	Cols. 22,23	Col. 26
0	SLATER	6	59	2

Card 2, format card for cards of type 1.

Cols. 1 to 32.

(1X, A5, 38I1, 2X, I3, 30X, I1 /

Card 3, format card for cards of type 2.

Cols. 1 to 30.

A6, 15I3, 3I2, 1X, 2I3, 2I1, 11X, I1)

The main data pack follows, and the closing card, punched with 999999999999999999 in columns one to thirty-six.

Here the main data pack contains 12 cards, 6 in each of the two types of format specified by cards 2 and 3. The input in this small program is restricted to integers.

Stage 2. If the program is restarted, or if there is no closing card present, the program goes on to read a number of control cards, and to form simple tables, one table for each control card that is read.

The layout of the control cards is;-

Col. 1	0	
Cols. 2 – 17	Name,	The name of the table, with up to 16 letters.
Col. 18	Switch digit.	This is 1 for a simple table, to add unity into cell I1, I2, I3 of the table,
	or	2 for a numeric table, to add IA(I3) into cell I1, I2 of the table,
	or	9 for a pause to stop the calculation.

Cols. 19 – 21 I1, the number of the first item to be counted.

22 – 24 J1, the maximum range of the first item.

25 – 27 I2, the number of the second item to be counted.

28 – 30 J2, the maximum range of the second item.

31 – 33 I3, the number of the third item to be counted.

34 – 36 J3, the maximum range of the third item.

The number of each item is its identifing number within one record. The range of an item is assumed to start at 0 and to go up in steps of 1 to the value given.

The program can form a one dimensional table of simple sums, a two dimensional table of one item against another item, or a three dimensional table of one item against another two items. The maximum number of cells in any one table is 600. Each record is set by the program to have a zero as its first item. The program normally forms a 3D table. If only a 2D table is required, J3 is set equal to 0, and I3 is set equal to the first item in the record, which is always zero. If only a 1D table is required, J2 and J3 are both set equal to 0, and I2 and I3 are both set equal to one, the number of the zero item in the record.

Example of a control card:

Col. 1	Cols. 2 – 17	Col. 18	Col. 21	Col. 24	Col. 27	Col. 30	Col. 33	Col. 36
0	TABLE 1 D6XD2	1	6	5	2	9	1	0

This card would control the formation of a two-dimensional table of size $(5 + 1) \times (9 + 1)$ of item number 6 against item number 2 of each record, assuming that item 1 for each record is always zero.

The upper limit on the number of items in one record is 100, and the upper limit on any range in a table is 20. The first column and the first row in each printed table, contain the sums of zero items. The last column but one contains the sum of the items in each row, and the last column in each printed table contains the percentage sums along the rows of the table. The last row but one in each table contains the column sums and the last row contains the percentage sums down the columns of the table. The last item on the last row but one contains the sum of all the items in the table.

The program uses one input, a card reader, one output, a line printer and one magnetic tape unit to store the data. It has only integer items in the store and it uses only about 4000 words of storage space, so that it can be used on a small, slow computer.

§4.5 Flow diagram for SURV

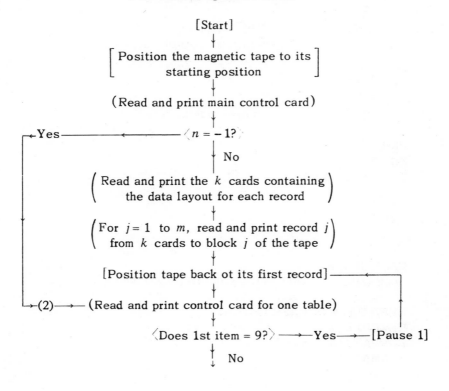

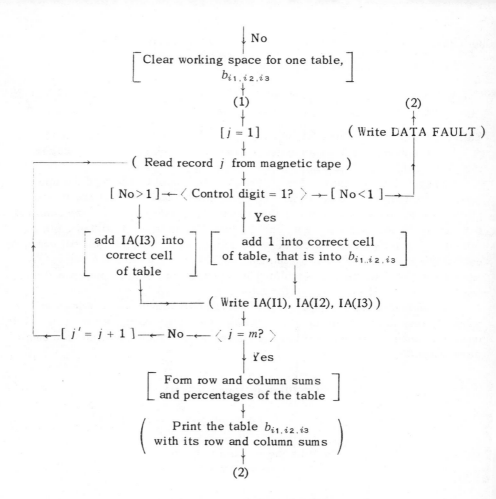

§4.6 Fortran program SURV

```
PROGRAM (SURV)
INPUT 1 = CR0
OUTPUT 2 = LP0

USE 3 = MT0
END



MASTER SURV
DIMENSION LAYOUT (80),IA(100),IB(600),NAME(2)

C       READ DATA IN FREE LAYOUT
        REWIND 3
1       FORMAT (1X,2A8, 3I3)
2       FORMAT (10A8)
```

```
        READ (1,1) NAME, M, N, K
        WRITE (2,1) NAME, M, N, K
        IF (N + 1) 0,18,0
        DO 5 I = 1,K
        READ (1,2) (LAYOUT(J + 10*I - 10), J = 1,10)
5       WRITE (2,2) (LAYOUT (J + 10*I - 10), J = 1,10)
        DO 3 J = 1,M
        READ (1,LAYOUT) (IA(I), I = 1,N)
        WRITE (2,9) IA(1),IA(2),IA(3)
        IA(1) = 0
3       WRITE (3) IA
10      REWIND 3

C       READ CODE CARD FOR ONE TABLE
4       FORMAT (1X,2A8,I1,6I3)
18      READ (1,4) NAME,IC,I1,J1,I2,J2,I3,J3
        IF (IC - 9) 13,0,13
6       PAUSE 1
        GO TO 10
13      WRITE (2,4) NAME,IC,I1,J1,I2,J2,I3,J3
        J1 = J1 + 1
        J2 = J2 + 1
        J3 = J3 + 1
15      N1 = J1*J2*J3
        DO 7 I = 1,N1
7       IB(I) = 0
        DO 8 J = 1,M
        READ (3) IA
        IF (IC - 1) 16,14,0
        L = IA(I1) + J1*IA(I2) + 1
        IB(L) = IB(L) + IA(I3)
        GO TO 8
14      L = IA(I1) + J1*IA(I2) + 1 + J1*J2* IA(I3)
        IB(L) = IB(L) + 1
8       WRITE (2,9) IA(I1),IA(I2),IA(I3)
9       FORMAT (1H, 3I4)
C       FORM ROW AND COLUMN SUMS AND PER CENTS
24      FORMAT (5H I3 = , I3/14H0 COL 0, 20 I 5)
        IF (IC - 1) 16,27,0
        J3 = 1
27      DO 23 I = 1,J3
        ID = I - 1
        JD = J2 - 1
        WRITE (2,24) I3, (J, J = 1,JD)
        DO 21 J = 1,100
21      IA(J) = 0
        IS = 0
        IM = J1*J2*I - J1 - J1*J2
```

151

```
        DO 19 J = 1, J2
        DO 20 K = 1, J1
        N1 = IB(K + J1*J + IM)
        IA(K) = IA(K) + N1
20      IA(50 + J) = IA(50 + J) + N1
19      IS = IS + IA(50 + J)
        DO 11 J = 1,J2
        N1 = IA(J + 50)*100/IS
        JD = J - 1
11      WRITE (2,12) JD,(IB(L + J1*J + IM), L = 1,J1), IA(J + 50), N1
12      FORMAT (5H ROW  ,23I5)
25      FORMAT (10H0 COL SUMS ,21I5)
        WRITE (2,25) (IA(J), J = 1,J2), IS
        DO 22 J = 1,J2
22      IA(J) = IA(J)*100/IS
26      FORMAT (10H0 PER CENT ,20I5)
23      WRITE (2,26) (IA(J), J = 1,J2)
        GO TO 10
16      WRITE (2,17)
        GO TO 6
17      FORMAT (11H DATA FAULT)
        END

        FINISH
```

§4.7 Sample of input and output of SURV

The input data pack is punched on the cards in this format:

OSLATER TEST DATA 3 54 2

This is the heading card of the main data pack. Three records of 54 items each. Two cards to one record.

(27I1/

Format card for cards of type 1.

27I1)

Format card for cards of type 2.

27 items occupying one column each.

111110001112223334445556667

Main data pack in correct order.

212221112223334445556667778

Record 1, cards 1 and 2.

123332223334445556667778889

Record 2, cards 1 and 2.

2211133344455566677788899 10

132224445556667778889910911

Record 3, cards 1 and 2.

233335556667778889910011912

999999999999999999999999999999999999

Card to cause pause at the end of reading the main data, punched with 36 9's.

OSLATER TABLE 1 1 27 9 54 9 1 0   Control card for the first table, to form a simple 2D table of item 27 range 0 to 9 against item 54, range 0 to 9.

OSLATER TABLE 2 2 27 9 54 9 26 9   Control card for the second table, to form a sum of item 26, range 0 to 9, in the table of item 27, range 0 to 9 against item 54, range 0 to 9.

99999999999999999999999999999999999999   Pause at the end of the tabulations.

The main data stream starts at column 1, the first column on the first card. It is very important indeed that the punching of the data cards is verified carefully and that the precise layout called for by the specification of the program is followed exactly. This small set of test data is typical of the small sample set of data which should be punched up and tested before any large sets of data are prepared, in order to provide a complete check on the accuracy and the layout of the data.

The output tables from the above data would be:

SLATER TEST DATA 3 54 2   Print of heading card, 3 records of 54 items each. Two cards to each record.

27I1/27I1)   Format of each record.

1	1	1
1	2	3
1	3	2

List of the first three items of data on all the records read.

SLATER TABLE 1 1 27 9 54 9 1 0   Control card defining the first table.

7	8	1
9	0	1
1	2	1

List of items to be tabulated.

I3 = 1   Table headings.

COL		0	1	2	3	4	5	6	7	8	9		
ROW	0	0	0	0	0	0	0	0	0	0	1	1	33
ROW	1	0	0	0	0	0	0	0	0	0	0	0	0
ROW	2	0	1	0	0	0	0	0	0	0	0	1	33
ROW	3	0	0	0	0	0	0	0	0	0	0	0	0
ROW	4	0	0	0	0	0	0	0	0	0	0	0	0
ROW	5	0	0	0	0	0	0	0	0	0	0	0	0
ROW	6	0	0	0	0	0	0	0	0	0	0	0	0
ROW	7	0	0	0	0	0	0	0	0	0	0	0	0
ROW	8	0	0	0	0	0	0	0	1	0	0	1	33
ROW	9	0	0	0	0	0	0	0	0	0	0	0	0
COL SUMS		0	1	0	0	0	0	0	1	0	1	3	
PER CENT		0	33	0	0	0	0	0	33	0	33		

153

In this first table, a 'one' has been added into cells (7,8), (9,0) and (1,2) of the table, one item from each of the three records in the test data. The row and column sums, the total sum and the row and column percentages have also been printed.

SLATER TABLE 2 2 27 9 54 9 26 9   Control card for the second table.

7	8	6	List of items to be tabulated.
9	0	8	
1	2	1	

I3 = 26   Table headings.

COL	0	1	2	3	4	5	6	7	8	9		
ROW 0	0	0	0	0	0	0	0	0	0	8	8	53
ROW 1	0	0	0	0	0	0	0	0	0	0	0	0
ROW 2	0	1	0	0	0	0	0	0	0	0	1	6
ROW 3	0	0	0	0	0	0	0	0	0	0	0	0
ROW 4	0	0	0	0	0	0	0	0	0	0	0	0
ROW 5	0	0	0	0	0	0	0	0	0	0	0	0
ROW 6	0	0	0	0	0	0	0	0	0	0	0	0
ROW 7	0	0	0	0	0	0	0	0	0	0	0	0
ROW 8	0	0	0	0	0	0	0	6	0	0	6	40
ROW 9	0	0	0	0	0	0	0	0	0	0	0	0
COL SUMS	0	1	0	0	0	0	0	6	0	8	15	
PER CENT	0	6	0	0	0	0	0	40	0	53		

In the second table, the actual items 6,8 and 1 from the 26'th position in each record have been added into the cells (7,8), (9,0) and (1,2) respectively.

Further reading on punched card equipment and on survey analysis will be found in C.A. Moser, (1960) *An Introduction to Social Surveys*, and J.S. Smith, (1960) *Punched Cards*.

Bibliography

Aitken A.C., (1956) *Determinants and Matrices*. Ninth edition. Oliver and Boyd, Edinburgh.

Allen R.G.D., (1938) *Mathematical Analysis for Economists*. Macmillan, London.

Barron D.W., and *Swinnerton-Dyer* H.P.F., (1960) Solution of simultaneous linear equations, *The Computer Journal* 3 pp. 28-33.

Bellman R., (1957) *Dynamic Programming*. University Press, Princeton, N.J.

Blackwell D., and *Girshik* M.A., (1954) *Theory of Games and Statistical Decisions*, Macmillan, London.

Brookes B.C., and *Dick* W.F.L., (1951) *Introduction to Statistical Method*. Heinemann, London.

Buckingham R.A., (1957) *Numerical Methods*. Pitman, London.

Casey R.S., *Perry* J.W., *Berry* M.M., and *Kent* A., (Editors) (1959) *Punched Cards*. Chapman and Hall, London.

Charnes A., *Cooper* W.W., and *Henderson* A., (1953) *An Introduction to Linear Programming*. McGraw Hill, New York.

Cooley W.W., and *Lohnes* P.R., (1960) *Multivariate Procedures in the Behavioral Sciences*. John Wiley, New York.

Cramer H., (1945) *Mathematical Methods of Statistics*, University Press, Princeton N.J.

Croxton F.E., and *Cowden* D.J., (1955) *Applied General Statistics*. Pitman, London.

Dantzig G.B., (1955) The generalized simplex method. *Pacific Journal* 5 (2) pp.183-195.

Dwight H.B., (1941) *Mathematical Tables*. Third edition. McGraw Hill, New York.

Dwyer P.S., (1951) *Linear Computations*. John Wiley, New York

Ezekiel M., (1941) *Methods of Correlation Analysis*. Second edition. John Wiley, New York.

Finney D.J., (1952) *Probit Analysis*. Second edition, Cambridge University Press, Cambridge.

Fisher R.A., and *Yates* F., (1957) *Statistical Tables*. Fifth edition, Oliver and Boyd, Edinburgh.

Fisher R.A., (1947) *The Design of Experiments*. Fourth edition, Oliver and Boyd, Edinburgh.

Fisher R.A., (1950) *Statistical Methods for Research Workers*. Eleventh edition, Oliver and Boyd, Edinburgh.

Fletcher A., *Miller* J.C.P., and *Rosenhead* L., (1962) *Index of Mathematical Tables*. Second edition, Scientific Computing Service, London.

Fox L., (1954) The practical inversion of matrices. *Applied Maths*. Series No. 39, National Bureau of Standards, Washington D.C.

Frazer R.A., *Duncan* W.J., and *Collier* A.R., (1946) *Elementary Matrices*. Cambridge University Press, Cambridge.

Freeman H., (1960) *Finite Differences*. Second edition. Cambridge University Press, Cambridge.

Frisch R., (1954) *Principles of Linear Programming*. Memorandum in Economics, The University Press, Oslo.

Gass S.I., (1958) *Linear Programming*. McGraw Hill, New York.

Goodwin E.T., (1961) *Modern Computing Methods*. Notes on Applied Science No. 16. H.M. Stationery Office, London.

Grable E.M., *Ramo* S., and *Wooldridge* D.E., (1958) *Handbook of Automation*. John Wiley, New York.

Hartree D.R., (1949) *Calculating Instruments and Machines*. University of Illinois Press, Urbana.

Hartree D.R., (1958) *Numerical Analysis*. Second Edition, Oxford University Press, Oxford.

Hastings C., (1952) *Approximations in Numerical Analysis*. The Rand Corporation, Los Angeles, California.

Hastings C., (1957) *Approximations for Digital Computers*. University Press, Princeton, N.J.

Heady E.O., and *Candler* W., (1958) *Linear Programming Methods*. University Press, Ames, Iowa.

Hollingdale F., and *Toothill* J., (1965) *Electronic Computers*. New Pelicans, London.

Hollingdale S.H., (1959) *High Speed Computing*. English Universities Press, London.

Jahnke F., and *Emde* F., (1952) *Tables of Higher Functions*. Fifth edition, Dover, New York.

Kendall M., (1943, 1946) *The Advanced Theory of Statistics*. Volumes I and II. Griffin, London.

Lance G.N., (1960) *Numerical Methods for High Speed Computers*. Iliffe, London.

Loveday R., (1960) *A First Course in Statistics*. Cambridge University Press, Cambridge.

Loveday R., (1961) *A Second Course in Statistics*. Cambridge University Press, Cambridge.

McCracken D.D., (1961) *A Guide to Fortran Programming*. John Wiley, New York.

McCracken D.D., and *Dorn* W.S., (1963) *Numerical Methods and Fortran Programming*, John Wiley, New York.

Montgomerie G.A., (1956) *Digital Calculating Machines*. Blackie, Glasgow.

Morgenstern O., (1950) *On the Accuracy of Economic Observations*. University Press, Princeton, N.J.

Nautical Almanac Office, (1956) *Interpolation and Allied Tables*. H.M. Stationery Office, London.

Nautical Almanac Office, (1958) *Subtabulation*. H.M. Stationery Office, London.

Neyman J., (1950) *A First Course in Probability and Statistics*. Holt, New York.

Pearson K., (1940) *Tables for Statisticians and Biometricians*. Cambridge University Press, Cambridge.

Pickforth C.N., (1946) *The Slide Rule*. Pitman, London.

Ralston A., and *Wilf* H.S., (1960) *Mathematical Methods for Digital Computers*. John Wiley, New York.

Samuelson P.A., (1947) *Foundations of Economic Analysis*. Harvard University Press, Cambridge, Mass.

Siddons A.W., *Snell* K.S., and *Lockwood* E.H., (1960) *A New Arithmatic for Schools*. Cambridge University Press, Cambridge.

Smith J.S., (1960) *Punched Cards*. MacDonald and Evans, London.

Stegun I.A., and *Abramovitz* M., (1956) Pitfalls in computation. *Journal Society of Industrial Applied Mathematics*. 4 pp.207-219.

Stone R., (1951) *The Role of Measurement in Economics*. Department of Applied Economics, Monograph No. 3, Cambridge University Press, Cambridge.

Tintner G., (1952) *Econometrics*. John Wiley, New York.

Vajda S., (1956) *The Theory of Games and Linear Programming*. Methuen, London.

Vajda S., (1958) *Readings in Linear Programming*. Pitman, London.

Varner W.W., (1957) *Computing with Desk Calculators*. Rinehart, New York.

Wald H., (1952) *Tables of Random Normal Deviates*. Tracts for Computers, No. 25, Cambridge University Press, Cambridge.

Weatherburn C.E., (1947) *A First Course in Mathematical Statistics*. Cambridge University Press, Cambridge.

Index

Date Due

JUL 25 73			
FEB 19 75			
JUN 20 1984			
OCT 31 1984			

DRAKE MEMORIAL LIBRARY
WITHDRAWN
THE COLLEGE AT BROCKPORT

DEMCO NO. 38-298